WATERBORNE AND RAIL TRANSPORT OF U.S. CRUDE OIL

ELEMENTS AND ISSUES

TRANSPORTATION ISSUES, POLICIES AND R&D

Additional books in this series can be found on Nova's website under the Series tab.

Additional e-books in this series can be found on Nova's website under the e-book tab.

TRANSPORTATION ISSUES, POLICIES AND R&D

WATERBORNE AND RAIL TRANSPORT OF U.S. CRUDE OIL

ELEMENTS AND ISSUES

PATRICK WILLIAMS
EDITOR

nova
publishers
New York

Library of Congress Cataloging-in-Publication Data

ISBN: 978-1-63463-003-0

Published by Nova Science Publishers, Inc. † New York

CONTENTS

PREFACE

New sources of crude oil from North Dakota, Texas, and western Canada have induced new routes for shipping crude oil to U.S. and Canadian refineries. While pipelines have traditionally been the preferred method of moving crude overland, they either are not available or have insufficient capacity to move all the crude from these locations. While rail has picked up some of this cargo, barges, and to a lesser extent tankers, also are moving increasing amounts of crude in domestic trade. This book discusses the Waterborne and rail transport of United States crude oil.

Chapter 1 - New sources of crude oil from North Dakota, Texas, and western Canada have induced new routes for shipping crude oil to U.S. and Canadian refineries. While pipelines have traditionally been the preferred method of moving crude overland, they either are not available or have insufficient capacity to move all the crude from these locations. While rail has picked up some of this cargo, barges, and to a lesser extent tankers, also are moving increasing amounts of crude in domestic trade.

The rather sudden shift in transportation patterns raises concerns about the safety and efficiency of oil tankers and barges. The United States now imports less oil than five years ago by oceangoing tankers, while more oil is moving domestically by river and coastal barges. However, the Coast Guard still lacks a safety inspection regime for barges similar to that which has long existed for ships. The possibility of imposing an hours-of-service limit for barge crews as part of this regime is controversial. Congress called for a barge safety inspection regime a decade ago, but the related rulemaking is not complete. The Coast Guard's progress in revamping its Marine Safety Office is a related issue that Congress has examined in the past.

The majority of U.S. refineries are located near navigable waters to take advantage of economical waterborne transport for both import and export. However, for refineries switching from imported to domestic crude oil, the advantage diminishes considerably. This is because the Jones Act, a 1920 law that seeks to protect U.S. shipyards and U.S. merchant sailors in the interest of national defense, restricts domestic waterborne transport to U.S.-built and - crewed vessels. The purchase price of U.S.-built tankers is about four times the price of foreign-built tankers, and U.S. crewing costs are several times those of foreign-flag ships. The small number of U.S.-built tankers makes it difficult for shippers to charter tankers for a short period or even a single voyage, highly desirable in an oil market with shifting supply patterns. The unavailability of U.S.-built tankers may result in more oil moving by costlier, and possibly less safe, rail transport than otherwise would be the case. Some Texas oil is moving to refineries in eastern Canada, bypassing refineries in the northeastern United States, because shipping to Canada on foreign-flag vessels is much cheaper than shipping domestically on Jones Act-eligible ships.

Some of these issues may be addressed in the Coast Guard and Maritime Transportation Act of 2014 (H.R. 4005), which has passed the House, and the Coast Guard Authorization Act for Fiscal Years 2015 and 2016 (S. 2444), introduced in the Senate. The House bill requests federal agency studies and recommendations towards improving the competitiveness of the U.S.-flag industry while the Senate bill contains provisions related to oil spill response.

Chapter 2 - North America is experiencing a boom in crude oil supply, primarily due to growing production in the Canadian oil sands and the recent expansion of shale oil production from the Bakken fields in North Dakota and Montana as well as the Eagle Ford and Permian Basins in Texas. Taken together, these new supplies are fundamentally changing the U.S. oil supply-demand balance. The United States now meets 66% of its crude oil demand from production in North America, displacing imports from overseas and positioning the United States to have excess oil and refined products supplies in some regions.

The rapid expansion of North American oil production has led to significant challenges in transporting crudes efficiently and safely to domestic markets—principally refineries—using the nation's legacy pipeline infrastructure. In the face of continued uncertainty about the prospects for additional pipeline capacity, and as a quicker, more flexible alternative to new pipeline projects, North American crude oil producers are increasingly turning to rail as a means of transporting crude supplies to U.S. markets. According to rail industry officials, U.S. freight railroads are estimated to have carried

434,000 carloads of crude oil in 2013 (roughly equivalent to 300 million barrels), compared to 9,500 carloads in 2008. In 2014, 650,000 carloads of crude oil are expected to be carried. Crude imports by rail from Canada have increased more than 20-fold since 2011. The amount of oil transported by rail may also be influenced by a tight market for U.S.-built tankers.

While oil by rail has demonstrated benefits with respect to the efficient movement of oil from producing regions to market hubs, it has also raised significant concerns about transportation safety and potential impacts to the environment. The most recent data available indicate that railroads consistently spill less crude oil per ton-mile transported than other modes of land transportation. Nonetheless, safety and environmental concerns have been underscored by a series of major accidents across North America involving crude oil transportation by rail—including a catastrophic fire that caused numerous fatalities and destroyed much of Lac Mégantic, Quebec, in 2013. Following that event, the U.S. Department of Transportation issued a safety alert warning that the type of crude oil being transported from the Bakken region may be more flammable than traditional heavy crude oil.

Legislation introduced in Congress following the Lac Mégantic disaster would require railroads to have at least two crew members aboard all trains. In addition, policy makers are discussing regulatory changes involving tank car design, prevention of derailments, and selection of preferred routes for transporting oil by rail. Congress may evaluate these changes in the reauthorization of the Rail Safety Improvement Act of 2008 (P.L. 110-432).

Chapter 3 - The dramatic increase in U.S. crude oil production, coupled with the increase in crude oil transport by rail, has raised questions about whether properties (e.g., flammability) of these crude types—particularly Bakken crude oil from North Dakota—differ sufficiently from other crude oils to warrant any additional handling considerations. The U.S. Pipeline and Hazardous Materials Safety Administration (PHMSA) issued a Safety Alert to notify emergency responders, shippers, carriers, and the public that recent derailments and resulting fires indicate that the type of crude oil transported from the Bakken region of North Dakota may be more flammable than traditional heavy crude oil. The alert reminds emergency responders that light sweet crude oil, such as that coming from the Bakken region, pose significant fire risk if released from the package (tank car) in an accident. PHMSA has expanded the scope of lab testing to include other factors that affect proper characterization and classification of crude oil such as volatility, corrosivity, hydrogen sulfide content and composition/concentration of the entrained gases in the material.

All crude oils are flammable, to a varying degree. Further, crude oils exhibit other potentially hazardous characteristics as well. The growing perception is that light volatile crude oil, like Bakken crude, is a root cause for catastrophic incidents and thus may be too hazardous to ship by rail. However, equally hazardous and flammable liquids from other sources are routinely transported by rail, tanker truck, barge, and pipeline, though not without accident.

A key question for Congress is whether the characteristics of Bakken crude oil make it particularly hazardous to ship by rail, or are there other causes of transport incidents, such as poor maintenance practices, inadequate safety standards, or human error.

Chapter 4 - The impacts of an oil spill depend on the size of the spill, the rate of the spill, the type of oil spilled, and the location of the spill. Depending on timing and location, even a relatively minor spill can cause significant harm to individual organisms and entire populations. Oil spills can cause impacts over a range of time scales, from days to years, or even decades for certain spills.

Based on data between 1973 and 2009, the annual number and volume of oil spills have shown declines—in some cases, dramatic declines. However, this trend was altered dramatically by the 2010 *Deepwater Horizon* oil spill in the Gulf of Mexico. The incident led to a significant release of oil: according to the federal government's estimate, the well released approximately 206 million gallons of oil before it was contained on July 15. The 2010 Gulf oil spill generated considerable interest in oil spill governance issues.

This report provides background information regarding oil spills in U.S. coastal waters and identifies the legal authorities governing oil spill prevention, response, and cleanup. The governing framework for oil spills in the United States remains a combination of federal, state, and international authorities. Within this framework, several federal agencies have the authority to implement oil spill regulations. Agency responsibilities can be divided into two categories: (1) oil spill response and cleanup and (2) oil spill prevention/preparedness.

Oil spill response authority is determined by the location of the spill: the U.S. Coast Guard has response authority in the U.S. coastal zone, and the Environmental Protection Agency covers the inland zone. Jurisdiction over oil spill prevention and preparedness duties is determined by the potential sources (e.g., vessels, facilities, pipelines) of oil spills.

As with the *Exxon Valdez* oil spill in 1989, the 2010 *Deepwater Horizon* spill generated significant attention to various oil spill policy matters, including prevention, preparedness, response, and liability and compensation. The 111th Congress enacted three oil spill-related proposals into law (P.L. 111-191, P.L. 111-212, and P.L. 111-281), but these laws generally concerned short-term matters that will not have a lasting impact on oil spill governance.

In general, oil spill-related issues garnered less attention during the 112th Congress. The 112th Congress enacted two statutes that contain oil spill-related provisions. P.L. 112-90 includes several oil spill-related provisions involving pipelines. P.L. 112-141 includes a subtitle referred to as the RESTORE Act. This act directs 80% of any administrative and civil Clean Water Act Section 311 penalties connected with the 2010 *Deepwater Horizon* oil spill into a newly created trust fund. Monies from this fund, through various mechanisms, will support environmental and economic restoration in the Gulf states.

In: Waterborne and Rail Transport of U.S. ...   ISBN: 978-1-63463-003-0
Editor: Patrick Williams   © 2014 Nova Science Publishers, Inc.

Chapter 1

SHIPPING U.S. CRUDE OIL BY WATER: VESSEL FLAG REQUIREMENTS AND SAFETY ISSUES*

John Frittelli

SUMMARY

New sources of crude oil from North Dakota, Texas, and western Canada have induced new routes for shipping crude oil to U.S. and Canadian refineries. While pipelines have traditionally been the preferred method of moving crude overland, they either are not available or have insufficient capacity to move all the crude from these locations. While rail has picked up some of this cargo, barges, and to a lesser extent tankers, also are moving increasing amounts of crude in domestic trade.

The rather sudden shift in transportation patterns raises concerns about the safety and efficiency of oil tankers and barges. The United States now imports less oil than five years ago by oceangoing tankers, while more oil is moving domestically by river and coastal barges. However, the Coast Guard still lacks a safety inspection regime for barges similar to that which has long existed for ships. The possibility of imposing an hours-of-service limit for barge crews as part of this regime is controversial. Congress called for a barge safety inspection regime a decade ago, but the related rulemaking is not complete. The Coast

---

* This is an edited, reformatted and augmented version of a Congressional Research Service publication, No. R43653, dated July 21, 2014.

Guard's progress in revamping its Marine Safety Office is a related issue that Congress has examined in the past.

The majority of U.S. refineries are located near navigable waters to take advantage of economical waterborne transport for both import and export. However, for refineries switching from imported to domestic crude oil, the advantage diminishes considerably. This is because the Jones Act, a 1920 law that seeks to protect U.S. shipyards and U.S. merchant sailors in the interest of national defense, restricts domestic waterborne transport to U.S.-built and -crewed vessels. The purchase price of U.S.-built tankers is about four times the price of foreign-built tankers, and U.S. crewing costs are several times those of foreign-flag ships. The small number of U.S.-built tankers makes it difficult for shippers to charter tankers for a short period or even a single voyage, highly desirable in an oil market with shifting supply patterns. The unavailability of U.S.-built tankers may result in more oil moving by costlier, and possibly less safe, rail transport than otherwise would be the case. Some Texas oil is moving to refineries in eastern Canada, bypassing refineries in the northeastern United States, because shipping to Canada on foreign-flag vessels is much cheaper than shipping domestically on Jones Act-eligible ships.

Some of these issues may be addressed in the Coast Guard and Maritime Transportation Act of 2014 (H.R. 4005), which has passed the House, and the Coast Guard Authorization Act for Fiscal Years 2015 and 2016 (S. 2444), introduced in the Senate. The House bill requests federal agency studies and recommendations towards improving the competitiveness of the U.S.-flag industry while the Senate bill contains provisions related to oil spill response.

INTRODUCTION

New sources of crude oil from the Bakken region of North Dakota, the Eagle Ford and Permian basins in Texas, and western Canada have induced new routes for shipping crude oil to U.S. and Canadian refineries.[1] While pipelines have traditionally been the preferred method of moving crude overland, especially to or from landlocked locations, they either are not available or have insufficient capacity to move all the crude from these new sources of production.[2] Although much of this oil is now moving to refineries by rail,[3] waterborne transportation is playing an increasing role in moving crude oil within North America.[4] The quantity of oil moving by barge on the Mississippi River and its tributaries increased ten-fold from 2009 to 2013, and tanker shipments between the Gulf Coast and Atlantic Canada have grown at an even faster rate (**Figure 1**). There are no current data on the amount of domestic crude oil moving by barge or tanker to refineries along the Gulf Coast, but it is believed to have increased significantly since 2012.

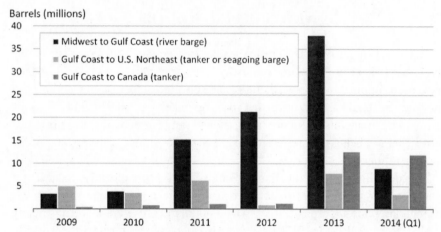

Source: U.S. Energy Information Administration.

Figure 1. Waterborne Crude Oil Movements between Selected Regions.

Two aspects of the oil industry critically influence shipping patterns: (1) not all crude oil is the same and (2) each refinery is currently equipped to refine a certain blend of crude oils. Refineries in the Northeast are predominantly configured to handle crudes from the Bakken, Eagle Ford, and Permian regions, but cannot efficiently refine oil sands crude from western Canada. There is greater variety in the capabilities of refineries on the Gulf and West Coasts. Reconfiguring a refinery to handle a different type of crude is possible but may be costly. The feasibility of doing so depends on the relative costs of various types of crude, the projected availability of the various crude oils, and the price spread between crude oil and refined petroleum products such as gasoline and diesel fuel.[5]

The sudden shift toward domestic sourcing of crude oil raises issues regarding the safety and efficiency of the maritime component of this new supply chain. These fall into two main categories. One concerns the Coast Guard's role in preventing oil spills by regulating the safety of vessels and the training and working conditions of crews.[6] The other has to do with the impact of the Jones Act, a 1920 law that restricts domestic waterborne transport to vessels built in the United States and crewed by U.S. citizens, which may now be affecting U.S. producers' decisions about how to ship crude oil and whether to send it to refineries in the United States or in Canada.

NEW SHIPPING ROUTES

The vast majority of U.S. refineries are located along the coast (including the Great Lakes) or an inland waterway. Most coastal refineries traditionally have been supplied by imported crude, and some lack pipeline connections and may not be equipped or have the space to receive crude by rail. For this reason, large amounts of oil are being moved out of production areas by truck or rail, but are being transferred to barges or tanker ships for the last leg of the trip to a refinery.

Crude oil produced at Eagle Ford, TX, is conveniently located for waterborne transport due to its proximity to the coast. Some of it moves through the port of Corpus Christi, where outbound crude oil shipments nearly trebled from 2012 to 2013.[7] The nearby port of Victoria, TX, has also experienced a dramatic increase in crude oil barge traffic. It appears that most of the Texas crude moving by vessel goes to coastal refineries in Texas and Louisiana or to the Louisiana Offshore Oil Port (LOOP), an offshore ship-to-pipeline transfer facility. A comparatively small amount of Eagle Ford crude oil moves by water to refineries in proximity to New York Harbor and the Delaware River, but much larger quantities seem to be going to refiners in Canada's Atlantic provinces.

While much of the oil coming from the Bakken region moves to refineries by rail, there are now several well-established intermodal routes involving water transport. These include:[8]

- rail to barge at St. Louis and Hayti, MO, and Osceola, AR, on the Mississippi River, to Gulf refineries;
- rail to barge at Hennepin, IL, on the Illinois Waterway, to Gulf refineries;
- rail to vessel at Albany, NY, on the Hudson River, to East Coast refineries;
- rail to Yorktown, VA, for coastal transport to East Coast refineries;
- rail to vessel at Anacortes and Vancouver, WA, for coastal transport to West Coast refineries.

Pipeline to barge transfer is occurring at Cushing, OK, from where barges move the oil down the Arkansas and Mississippi Rivers to Gulf Coast refineries.

VESSEL TYPES AND CAPACITIES

New waterborne services moving crude oil from the Bakken or Texas generally do so with smaller vessels than the trans-oceanic tankers used to carry Alaskan and imported oil. The fleet can be divided into two broad categories: "brownwater" vessels operating on inland and near-shore waters and "bluewater" vessels operating in the open ocean.

A river barge can hold 10,000 to 30,000 barrels of oil.[9] Two to three river barges are typically tied together in a single tow, and thus a river tow of tank barges could carry 20,000 to 90,000 barrels. In addition to inland rivers, this type of barge configuration is used on the intracoastal waterway (an inland canal) along the coasts of Texas and Louisiana. River barges have speeds of about 4 to 5 miles per hour (mph).

A coastal tank barge designed for open seas (an articulated tug-barge, or ATB)[10] can hold 50,000 to 185,000 barrels. However, newer ATBs can carry 240,000 to 340,000 barrels, a capacity comparable to that of coastal tankers. Seagoing barges have speeds of about 10 knots (12 mph).

In contrast to coastal tank barges, a river barge can be used in "drop and swap" operation—that is, the tugboat can drop a loaded barge at a facility where it can be used for storing product while the tugboat is free to make other barge movements—so that the relatively expensive self-propelled portion of the vessel is not tied up while unloading, as a tank ship would be. The tugs designed for ATBs sail poorly without the barge, so they seldom perform drop and swap operations.[11]

A coastal tank ship can hold 300,000 to 650,000 barrels. The coastal tankers that are being deployed to move Texas crude carry 330,000 barrels and are referred to as "handysize" or "medium range" tankers. Coastal tankers have speeds of about 12-15 knots.

For comparison, tankers moving Alaska oil to the West Coast carry between 800,000 and 1.3 million barrels of oil and fall into the "Aframax" or "Suezmax" size categories. Very large or ultra-large crude carriers (VLCCs and ULCCs) that carry imported oil from overseas hold 2 to 3 million barrels. A crude oil pipeline moves between 400,000 and 800,000 barrels per day, enough to service the largest U.S. refineries. The unit trains[12] that move

Bakken and Texas crude oil can carry 70,000 to 80,000 barrels. **Table 1** summarizes conveyances for moving domestic crude oil.

Table 1. U.S. Crude Oil Conveyances

Conveyance	Capacity (000 barrels)	Cruising Speed	Crew Size	Inventory	Operating Geography
River barge	20-90	4-5 mph	4-10	3,500-4,000*	inland rivers, intracoastal waterway
Seagoing barge (ATB)	50-300	10 knots (12 mph)	6-12	86*	coastal U.S.
Handysize product tanker	300	12-15 knots (14-18 mph)	21-28	31*	coastal U.S.
Aframax or Suezmax crude oil tanker	800-1,300	12-15 knots (14-18 mph)	21-28	11* 1,400 (foreign-flag)	Alaska to Puget Sound and California, U.S. Gulf Coast to Eastern Canada
100-car unit train	70-80	40-50 mph	2	45,000 crude oil tank cars/450 unit trains**	continental U.S., predominantly west-east
Crude oil pipeline	400-800	3-8 mph	1-2 (remote monitors)	57,500 miles	predominantly midcontinent, south-north, Alaska

Source: U.S. Department of Transportation; Army Corps of Engineers; Clarkson Research Services Ltd. *Tanker Register.*

Notes: *For domestic service, vessels must be U.S. built and U.S. flagged. **Tank car inventory increasing rapidly.

As **Table 1** indicates, the Jones Act-eligible fleet of crude oil tankers consists of 11 ships, all employed in moving Alaska crude oil to the U.S. West Coast or to a refinery in Alaska. Of the 86 seagoing barges, 42 can carry more than 130,000 barrels. While a tanker's capacity is better matched to the daily consumption rates of a single refinery than the capacity of a unit train or most barges, the limited fleet of Jones Act-eligible tankers has required some refineries with direct ocean access to ship domestic oil by barge or train or to continue to rely on foreign sources.

Jones Act-qualified ATBs and product tankers are also used to lighter ocean-going crude oil tankers.[13] Although it is technically feasible to do so, tank vessels do not readily alternate between carrying dirty oil (crude oil, residual fuel oil, asphalt) and refined (clean) petroleum products because the tanks would have to be extensively washed after carrying dirty product, a time-consuming and costly process. However, due to the recent increase in domestic crude oil production, particularly at Eagle Ford, some tonnage has shifted from the "clean" products trade to the crude oil trade.[14] Tankers that used to carry refined product from the Gulf Coast to Florida (via the Port of Tampa) are now carrying crude oil because they can earn higher returns.[15] Barges are replacing them to move refined products to Florida, a development that has been blamed for higher gasoline prices in Florida.[16]

The decline of oil imports from overseas may free up some of the lightering fleet for the domestic crude trade. If West Coast refineries source more crude from the Bakken or Canada rather than Alaska, this could also free up Jones Act tankers. One such tanker is believed to have been redeployed to move crude oil from the Gulf of Mexico to the West Coast via the Panama Canal.[17] However, there is a limit to how many clean product tankers will switch to carrying crude oil. The crude oil boom has also led to a boom in U.S. refinery output, so there is also strong demand for clean product tankers.

Vessel Size Relates to Voyage Distance

The most economic tank vessel size to deploy depends largely on voyage distance. The longer the voyage, the more incentive there is to use a larger vessel because of economies of scale at sea. The first VLCCs were built when the Suez Canal was closed in the late 1960s and tankers headed from the Persian Gulf to Europe and North America had to sail longer routes around South Africa.

Larger tankers face diseconomies of scale in port: they take longer to load and unload than smaller ships, and some port charges are based on vessel size. Thus, smaller vessels are used for shorter voyages, on which a tanker will spend a greater portion of its total time in port. Aframax and Suezmax tankers, considered of medium size, are being used to ship Alaska oil from Valdez to Seattle, a distance of 1,200 nautical miles, and to Los Angeles, a distance of 2,000 nautical miles. Similar tankers carry Texas oil to eastern Canadian refineries with sailing distances ranging from 2,300 to 3,000 nautical miles.[18]

Evidence from these other trades suggests that Aframax or Suezmax tankers would be the preferred vessels for shipments from Texas ports to Delaware River and New York Harbor oil terminals, a distance of 1,900 to 2,000 nautical miles, if such tankers were available in the Jones Act-eligible fleet. The handysize tankers that are now used for this purpose may be smaller than the preferred size. Prior to carrying crude oil, these handysize tankers were moving refined product on much shorter *intra*coastal voyages, such as from Houston to Tampa. From 2001 to 2011 (before the Texas and Bakken oil boom began) the average haul of Jones Act handysize product tankers was roughly 1,000 nautical miles while the average haul for the larger Jones Act Aframax and Suezmax crude oil tankers was roughly 1,700 nautical miles.[19]

ATBs are used on much shorter coastal voyages. From 2001 to 2011, their average haul was about 420 nautical miles (the approximate sailing distance between Norfolk, VA, and Charleston, SC). Since they are somewhat slower than tankers, on longer voyages they could require an additional day or two to reach destination. However, newer ATBs, which can be larger and faster, tend to be deployed on longer voyages. In 2010, coastal tank barges that were less than 10 years old accounted for 63% of overall coastal barge shipments less than 500 miles but 70% of the shipments 500 miles or more.[20]

MARITIME SAFETY ISSUES

The large increase in domestic waterborne shipment of crude oil and refined products comes at a time when the Coast Guard is reevaluating its regulations and industry oversight. Several new regulations are pending.

New Barge Safety Regime

Barges are the workhorses in moving Bakken and Texas oil by water. However, the Coast Guard has just begun establishing a safety inspection regime for barges.

In the Coast Guard and Maritime Transportation Act of 2004 (P.L. 108-293, §415), Congress directed the Coast Guard to establish a barge safety inspection and certification regime similar to that which exists for ships. This includes establishing structural standards for vessels as well as standards for the crew. This new inspection regime will be more significant for tank barges used on rivers than for seagoing barges, because seagoing barges moving oil or other hazardous material are already inspected.[21] However, one pending rule would also apply to seagoing barges. Section 409 of the 2004 act authorized the Coast Guard to evaluate an hours-of-service limit for crews on towing vessels. This was in line with a 1999 National Transportation Safety Board (NTSB) recommendation that the Coast Guard establish scientifically based hours-of-service regulations for domestic vessel operators.[22]

On August 11, 2011, the Coast Guard issued a notice of proposed rulemaking on barge inspections and work hours.[23] In the notice, the Coast Guard states that on a schedule providing six hours of work followed by six hours of rest, as is typical on barges engaged in multi-day voyages, sleep debt accumulates and gradually increases crew members' fatigue levels.[24] ATB operators have filed comments opposed to addressing hours of service as part of this rulemaking, while maritime unions have filed comments in favor of a mandatory eight-hour rest period.[25] The NTSB filed comments reiterating its support of an eight-hour rest period. The Coast Guard has not issued final regulations.

Crewing Requirements of ATBs vs. Tankers

According to an original designer of the ATB, "The American coastwise shipping business has grown in a way that differs from many other nations. The high cost of manning and building ships has led over the years to a coastwise transportation network dominated by tugs and barges."[26] ATBs are sometimes referred to as "rule breakers" within the maritime industry because they operate with smaller crews.[27] The Coast Guard determines crewing requirements based on the registered tonnage of a vessel, which for barges includes only the tug, not the barges the tug may be pushing. As a result, the crew required aboard an ATB is one-third to one-half the number required aboard a tank ship; an ATB typically has a crew of 6 to 12, versus 21 to 28 for a tank ship. (The precise number for each vessel type depends on the amount of automation.)

The Coast Guard's pending decision on hours of service could force ATBs to carry larger crews, possibly negating their economic advantage compared to tankers. This occurred previously with a precursor to the ATB called the integrated tug barge: when the Coast Guard increased their manning requirements in 1981, integrated tug barges lost their economic advantage, and none have been built since.[28] The Coast Guard increased manning requirements because integrated tug barges operated essentially as ships since the tug and barge seldom separated. While ATBs are designed for easier separation of tug and barge, as noted earlier, they also seldom separate.

The distinction in crewing requirements between ships and ATBs has been criticized for distorting the domestic shipping market by encouraging the use of otherwise less efficient (and perhaps less militarily useful) barges instead of ships.[29] A counterargument is that the problem is not the small crew size on ATBs but the excessive manning requirements for coastal tankers.

Pace of Rulemaking an Issue for Congress

Congress has been concerned with the pace at which the Coast Guard is issuing barge safety regulations under the 2004 law. In the Coast Guard Authorization Act of 2010 (P.L. 111-281, §701), Congress requested that all rulemakings related to oil pollution prevention, including barge inspection, be finalized within 18 months of enactment (i.e., by April 15, 2012). The 2010 act (§702) also required the Coast Guard to promulgate additional regulations to reduce the risk of oil spills in operations involving the transfer of oil from or to a tank vessel. The Coast Guard has issued a request for public comments, but has not yet proposed regulations.[30]

Performance of the Coast Guard's Marine Safety Office

The Coast Guard's ability to provide effective safety oversight of certain maritime operations has been a long-standing concern. In response to questions raised by Congress in 2007,[31] the Coast Guard acknowledged that its practice of regularly rotating staff geographically or by activity, as military organizations typically do, was hindering its ability to develop a cadre of staff with sufficient technical expertise in marine safety.[32] In response, the agency created additional civilian safety positions, converted military positions into civilian ones, and developed a long-term career path for civilian safety inspectors and investigators.[33] Despite these changes, at an October 2011 meeting to discuss inspection regulations towing operators complained about having to rehash the same issues with a "revolving door" of Coast Guard officials.[34] They also asserted that the Coast Guard was placing too much emphasis on a one-day-per-year inspection of vessels and equipment and not enough emphasis on human factors, the leading cause of marine accidents.

The number and quality of the Coast Guard's investigations and reports of marine accidents, as well as the lack of a "near-miss" reporting system, have been noted by the Department of Homeland Security Inspector General (IG) and other observers as missed opportunities to learn from past incidents. A May 2013 IG audit concluded:[35]

> The USCG does not have adequate processes to investigate, take corrective actions, and enforce Federal regulations related to the reporting of marine accidents. These conditions exist because the USCG has not developed and retained sufficient personnel, established a complete process with dedicated resources to address corrective actions, and provided adequate training to personnel on enforcement of marine accident reporting. As a result, the USCG may be delayed in identifying the causes of accidents; initiating corrective actions; and providing the findings and lessons learned to mariners, the public, and other government entities. These conditions may also delay the development of new standards, which could prevent future accidents.

The IG found that at the 11 sites it visited, two-thirds of accident inspectors and investigators did not meet the Coast Guard's own qualification standards. The IG noted that the shortage of qualified personnel would be further compounded by the new towing vessel safety regime, which would expand the inspections workload. In response to this audit, the Coast Guard stated it was developing a "Maritime Prevention Enhancement Plan" that it hoped to complete in FY2014. In the Coast Guard Authorization Act of 2010 (P.L. 111-281, §521), Congress requested an annual report from the Coast Guard assessing the adequacy of its marine safety workforce.[36]

THE JONES ACT

The Jones Act requires that vessels transporting cargo between two U.S. points be built in the United States, crewed by U.S. citizens, and at least 75% owned by U.S. citizens.[37] The law was enacted in 1920 (Merchant Marine Act of 1920, §27, P.L. 66-261).[38] One of the motivations for the U.S.-build requirement was to facilitate the disposal of cargo ships constructed during World War I by the U.S. Shipping Board, a government agency set up in 1916 to purchase, construct, and operate merchant ships during the war. The Jones Act authorized the sale of these vessels to the private sector.[39]

The Jones Act stated an explicit national policy of supporting a U.S. merchant marine and a U.S. shipbuilding industry in the interest of national defense. That policy remains in the law today:[40]

It is necessary for the national defense and the development of the domestic and foreign commerce of the United States that the United States have a merchant marine (1) sufficient to carry the waterborne domestic commerce and a substantial part of the waterborne export and import foreign commerce of the United States and to provide shipping service essential for maintaining the flow of waterborne domestic and foreign commerce at all times; (2) capable of serving as a naval and military auxiliary in time of war or national emergency; (3) owned and operated as vessels of the United States by citizens of the United States; (4) composed of the best-equipped, safest, and most suitable types of vessels constructed in the United States and manned with a trained and efficient citizen personnel; and (5) supplemented by efficient facilities for building and repairing vessels.

Because of the restrictions on shipbuilding and crewing, Jones Act ships tend to be more costly to build and operate than vessels used by foreign-flag ocean carriers, which can order vessels from whichever shipyards offer the lowest bids and typically hire most of their crew members from countries where seafarers' wages are much lower than in the United States.

Jones Act Shipping Rates

According to oil shippers, the price for moving crude oil from the Gulf Coast to the U.S. Northeast on Jones Act tankers is $5 to $6 per barrel, while moving it to eastern Canada on foreign-flag tankers is $2.[41] For a Texas oil producer using a tanker with capacity of 300,000 barrels, this rate difference amounts to receiving $1 million less for a shipment of oil to a U.S. refinery than for a shipment to a more distant Canadian refinery. In consequence, from January 2013 through March 2014, more than twice as much Gulf Coast crude oil was shipped by water to Canada as was shipped to U.S. Northeast refineries.

Refineries in the U.S. Northeast consumed about 12 times as much crude oil from fields offshore of eastern Canada as oil shipped from the Gulf Coast in all of 2013. They also consumed imports from Nigeria, Saudi Arabia, and other countries. Shipping rates for these imports, regardless of country of origin, are much lower than domestic shipping rates for Gulf Coast oil (**Table 2**).[42] (Shipping oil from the Gulf Coast to eastern Canada costs more than shipping it from Africa to the U.S. Northeast because ice-class tankers must be used to serve Canadian refineries for a portion of the year.)

Table 2. Ocean Shipping Rates to U.S. Northeast Refineries
Dollars per barrel

Origin	Estimated Rate
U.S. Gulf Coast	$5.00-$6.00
Eastern Canada	$1.20
Nigeria	$1.45-$1.70
Saudi Arabia	$1.90

Source: *Platts Oilgram News*, "Regulation and Environment," September 9, 2013; *Platts OilGram Price Report*, McGraw Hill Financial, January-April, 2014.

Although there is currently no Bakken oil moving from Washington or Oregon ports to California refineries, the cost aboard a Jones Act tanker is estimated to be $4 to $5 per barrel; as the oil would have to move from the Bakken region to the ports by rail at a cost of about $9 per barrel, the total shipping cost would be $13 to $14 per barrel. The cost of shipping Eagle Ford oil through the Panama Canal to these refineries is estimated to be $10 per barrel.[43] By comparison, shipping oil from Ecuador to West Coast refineries costs around $3.25 per barrel, and Iraqi oil about $2.30 per barrel.[44]

Jones Act rates for shipping Alaska oil to West Coast refineries are not available, but Bakken oil shipped by rail to Pacific Northwest refineries is beginning to displace Alaskan oil. Alaska oil producers could look to resume exports to Asia to replace lost shipments to the U.S. West Coast. However, as specified by Congress when it lifted the export ban on Alaska North Slope oil in 1995 (P.L. 104-58), the oil must be exported on U.S.-crewed and -flagged tankers, although the tankers do not need to be U.S. built. After the Alaska export ban was lifted, roughly 5%-7% of Alaskan oil was exported, mostly to South Korea, Japan, and China, but exports ceased in 2000.[45]

In the case of crude oil, the price coastal refineries are willing to pay is based on the international price of oil, as a refinery has no way to raise the prices of gasoline and other refined products if its transportation costs are higher than those of its competitors. In order to minimize transportation costs, U.S. oil shippers have favored barges over ships for coastwise transport, but this may have reduced the shipment distances over which domestic waterborne oil is price competitive. The long-term decline in the amount of petroleum carried domestically by tankers is reflected in the diminished capacity of the privately owned Jones Act-eligible tanker fleet (see **Figure 2**). Following World War II, the relatively small U.S.-flag tankers in international service were gradually replaced by much larger foreign-built tankers. Many of the Jones Act-eligible tankers in domestic service were replaced by tank barges

following enactment of a double-hull requirement for tank vessels in the Oil
Pollution Act of 1990. The decline of oil production in Alaska, which has
fallen by about 46% over the last decade, also contributed to reduced demand
for Jones Act-eligible crude oil tankers, causing some to be scrapped.

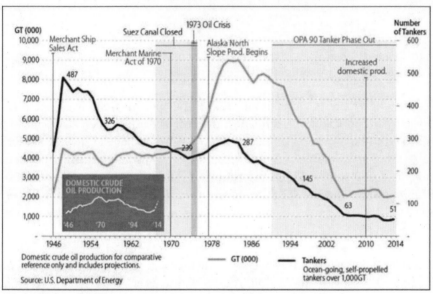

Source: CRS modification of figure from U.S. Maritime Administration.
Notes: GT= gross tonnage, an indication of the cargo capacity of a ship. Figures
        pertain to both Jones Act (domestic) and international tankers.

Figure 2. U.S.-Flag Privately-Owned Tanker Fleet.

Domestic Tanker Construction Costs

According to data from the U.S. Maritime Administration (MARAD), an
agency of the U.S. Department of Transportation, and from industry sources,
the cost of domestically built tankers is approximately four times the cost of
tankers of similar size built in foreign shipyards (**Table 3**). Almost all
oceangoing tankers are built in Asia; in 2012, Korean shipyards received 60%
of worldwide orders for new tankers, Chinese yards 30%, and Japanese yards
8% (measured by ship capacity). U.S. shipyards' prices are higher even though
major ship components, like the engines, are built in foreign yards. The
purchase price of new river tugs and barges in the United States is not

considered to be as great a deterrent to river transport, perhaps because barges are simpler to build and are ordered in sufficient quantities that shipyards can achieve some economies of scale.[46]

Table 3. U.S. and World Prices for Tanker Vessels
(Cost of a newbuild, based on recent deliveries or construction contract announcements)

Vessel Type	Capacity	U.S. Price	World Price
Handysize product tanker (aka medium-range tanker)	40,000-50,000 dwt 330,000 bbl	$100-$135 million	$30-$35 million
Ocean-going ATB (smaller)	27,000 dwt 185,000 bbl	$60-$85 million	not available
Ocean-going ATB (larger)	45,000 dwt 250,000-300,000 bbl	$100-$130 million	not available
Aframax tanker	80,000-120,000 dwt 650,000-800,000 bbl	$200 million	$45-$55 million
Suezmax tanker	130,000-160,000 dwt 1 million bbl	No recent builds	$55-$65 million
Very Large Crude Carrier (VLCC)	200,000-320,000 dwt 2 million bbl	No recent builds	$90-$100 million

Source: U.S. Maritime Administration, Title XI Ship Financing Guarantees, Pending and Approved Loan Applications; American Petroleum Tankers S-1 SEC Filing; RBN Energy LLC; RS Platou Economic Research, annual and monthly reports; press releases from Kinder Morgan, Teekay Tankers, Scorpio Tankers, Euronav; Poten and Partners, *Weekly Tanker Opinion*.

As **Table 3** indicates, tank ships are more expensive to build than ATBs. They require more scantling (interior framing) and more freeboard (the height of the hull from the water to the deck) than barges. However, tank ships have significant advantages over barges. They can operate in more adverse weather conditions than ATBs, are faster, and have superior fuel economy. The U.S. Energy Information Administration estimated in 2012 that the cost of moving crude oil from the Gulf Coast to Northeast refineries by tanker would be about half the cost of moving it by barge— not counting the cost of construction.[47] This suggests that tankers could have a competitive advantage over barges on longer coastal voyages if domestic shipbuilding costs were lower or if foreign-built tankers could be employed.

The Tariff Act of 1930 (19 U.S.C. §1466), requires that U.S.-flag ships pay a 50% *ad valorem* duty on any non-emergency repairs conducted in foreign shipyards. A 2011 MARAD study[48] of ships operating in international trade found that ship repair costs for U.S.-flag ships are 1.3 times those of foreign-flag ships. The MARAD study found that many U.S. ships have repairs performed in foreign yards because, even with the 50% duty, the total cost is less than if the repairs were performed in a U.S. domestic shipyard.

U.S.-Flag Vessel Operating Costs

A 2011 MARAD study comparing U.S.-flag versus foreign-flag operating costs in international trade found that U.S.-flag vessels' operating costs were substantially higher—2.7 times higher. (This higher operating cost does not reflect higher domestic construction costs, because U.S.-flag ships engaging in international trade do not have to be built in the United States.) The study estimated the average daily operating cost of a foreign-flag ship to be under $6,000.[49] A separate MARAD study in June 2012 estimated the daily operating cost of a Jones Act tanker to be $22,000, which would be about 3.7 times the operating cost of a foreign-flag tanker. A major reason U.S.-flag vessels cost more to operate is that they are crewed by U.S. citizens. The crews on most foreign-flag ships are drawn mainly from poor countries and are paid significantly less than U.S. merchant seafarers.

According to MARAD, the daily operating cost of an ATB ($13,000) is almost half that of a U.S.- flag tanker ($22,000).[50] Since an ATB might travel two to three knots slower than a tanker, it might require additional sailing time. On a voyage from Texas to New York, an ATB would require two additional sailing days, reducing the ATB's cost savings over a tanker to about one-quarter, assuming that the vessels carry similar amounts of oil. However, only five ATBs in the Jones Act fleet match the capacity of a handysize tanker (330,000 barrels). Most ATBs now in use carry half as much oil as a tanker, thus requiring two voyages to match the capacity of a tanker; their operating cost per barrel of oil on this comparatively long voyage is likely to be higher than that of a tanker. A large tanker carrying oil from Nigeria to the U.S. East Coast, requiring two weeks sailing time, would be expected to have lower overall operating costs and lower operating costs per barrel than a U.S.-flag tanker ship or ATB making the much shorter domestic voyage.

The Missing Triangle Trade
One consequence of the relatively high cost of building and operating Jones Act tankers is that they cannot compete effectively for international cargo. This results in Jones Act tankers sailing empty much of the time, further raising shipowners' costs.

A key aspect to improving the economic competitiveness of freight carriers is reducing empty travel miles. If Jones Act product tankers were price competitive in the international market, they could triangulate their trade routes, perhaps moving diesel fuel from Gulf Coast refineries to Europe, then carrying European gasoline to the U.S. Atlantic Coast before sailing in ballast (carrying only ballast water for stability) to the Gulf Coast to repeat.[51] In this triangular route, two out of three voyages would generate revenue and the ballast sailing distance would amount to 18% of the total sailing distance. With their costs rendering them uncompetitive on international routes, however, Jones Act product tankers typically sail "piston" routes, carrying crude oil or refined products from the Gulf Coast to the East Coast and then returning in ballast, thus earning revenue on only half the trip.

A peculiar triangular trade has developed to circumvent the Jones Act requirements. This involves Gulf Coast refineries shipping gasoline to the Bahamas, where additives are mixed in before the product is moved to the U.S. Northeast. So long as the product is processed in the Bahamas, both water movements can be made in foreign-flag tankers.[52] The savings from using foreign-flag shipping are apparently greater than the cost of an additional tanker unloading and loading operation.

Chartering and the Jones Act
Because of the Jones Act, U.S. oil shippers also cannot take advantage of the current surplus in the world tanker fleet, caused in part by the drop-off in crude oil shipments to the United States. If it were accessible, chartering could be done on a spot basis (for a single voyage) or on a time basis (for six months to two years). Given the rapid changes in the U.S. oil market, some shippers might prefer the flexibility of chartering to the long-term financial commitment required to build a pipeline or a rail terminal. However, the number of Jones Act-qualified tankers is small, and most appear to be tied up in charters lasting several years. Current Jones Act charter rates are $75,000 to $100,000 per day, up from about $50,000 per day in the 2010 through 2012 period.[53] In the world market, charter rates for tankers of similar size ("medium range") have fluctuated around $10,000 per day for spot charters and $15,000 per day for 12-month time charters.[54]

A spot market is also valuable because it lowers the overall cost of moving oil for everyone by adding fluidity to tanker supply. For instance, the sailing times of tankers cannot always be synchronized exactly with loading schedules. If an oil company's tanker is two weeks early for a shipment, rather than idling its tanker for that time, the company can re-let the tanker in the spot market for someone else's use. The oil company could then charter someone else's tanker for its intended shipment. In other words, by pooling the tanker supply in the spot market, the fleet is used more efficiently. By segregating the domestic shipping market from the international market, the Jones Act undermines a competitive advantage of tankers against pipelines, namely their status as mobile assets that can be redeployed in response to market changes.

Waterborne vs. Pipeline

Before the advent of oil produced from shale deposits and its movement by rail, tank vessels and pipelines were the primary options for moving oil. Both modes can move crude oil to refineries in lot sizes of hundreds of thousands of barrels, fitting a large refinery's daily intake needs. Economies of scale are important to both, but installing a larger pipe reduces the transportation cost per barrel more rapidly for pipelines than building a larger vessel does for ship lines. For this reason, oil companies typically share use of a large pipeline rather than building smaller individual pipelines. Pipelines face a disadvantage in that they must acquire, build, maintain, and pay property taxes on their rights of way, not only for the pipe but also for the pumping stations, whereas navigation infrastructure in harbors (shipping channels) and on inland waterways (locks and dams) is largely provided by the federal government. As indicated in **Table 1**, pipelines move product between 3 and 8 mph, so tankers have a speed advantage. This can be important when oil prices are volatile. On the other hand, pipelines are extremely dependable in delivering product on time, so little safety stock is needed.

Economies of Scale Diverge
Over recent decades, pipeline operators have managed to ship more oil with less pipe. Pipeline mileage leveled off in the 1980s. Since then, miles of trunk line have actually decreased but capacity has increased because the pipes are larger in diameter.[55] The amount of oil carried per mile of trunk line pipe is about 37% higher today than it was in the 1980s.

In contrast, Jones Act carriers are utilizing smaller, rather than larger, vessels to transport oil, a result of increasingly relying on barges rather than tankers in coastwise transport. In 1980, barges represented 39% of the total cargo capacity of the tank vessel fleet (barges and tankers).[56] In 2012, barges accounted for 82% of the total cargo capacity and carried about 65% of the coastwise refined product tonnage. The shift from tankers to barges is significant, because what should be the least-cost method for transporting crude oil and petroleum products is being utilized less than it might be in favor of a method that is cost-competitive due only to regulation.

The divergence in economies of scale between the pipeline and waterborne modes parallels a trend in their respective modal shares. In 1979, pipelines handled 58% of crude oil shipments (measured in ton-miles)[57] and waterborne carriers 41%. For refined products, 44% moved by pipeline and 48% by water. By 2009, pipelines were carrying 80% of crude oil shipments to 19% for ships and barges, and 63% of refined products movements went by pipeline as opposed to 26% by water.[58] Part of the reason for the change in modal share in refined product was a sharp decline in use of residual fuel oil for heat and power, which affected waterborne market share.[59] Today, tanker ships are used in domestic trade primarily where there is no pipeline service, as with crude oil shipments from Alaska to the lower 48 states and gasoline shipments from the Gulf Coast to Florida.

Pipelines appear to be preferred over river transport as well. Pipelines are used heavily to move Gulf Coast crude oil north to the Upper Midwest, carrying about 30 million barrels a month, whereas barges do not carry any crude oil upriver on the Mississippi waterway system. Barges have less than 10% of the market for refined products moving between the Gulf Coast and the Upper Midwest.

Waterborne vs. Pipeline for Coastal Transport of Refined Products

Since production of refined products is more geographically dispersed than it is for crude oil, the competition between tanker and pipeline for moving refined products is more prevalent. A shift in relative costs between the two modes can change modal shares significantly, as happened in the early 1960s when the Colonial Pipeline was built.

By far the highest volume domestic route for shipping U.S. petroleum liquids is from the Gulf Coast to the Northeast. The U.S. government built two pipelines along the East Coast during World War II

---

after German submarines sank 48 U.S. coastal tankers in four months. After the war, the pipelines were sold to private interests, and one was converted to natural gas. Despite the pipeline, the route continued to be the most important for U.S.-flag product tankers.

In the summer of 1961, U.S. seafarers staged an 18-day strike which idled 114 ships on the Gulf to East Coast run. It ended with a federal injunction, but with issues mostly unsettled. U.S. seafarers achieved higher wages but no success against using foreign-flag tankers to import oil. In 1962, nine oil companies announced plans to build a 22" to 36" pipeline from Houston to New York Harbor to move 600,000 barrels a day of refined product. The oil companies cited maritime strike disruptions and higher seafarer wages, along with new pipeline technology allowing for larger-diameter pipe, as reasons why the pipeline would be more economical than ships. The maritime industry estimated the pipeline would take one-third of its cargo and reduce fleet size by 50 tankers. The need for the pipeline depended upon continuation of federal restrictions on the amount of oil that could be imported. It was believed that if the import restrictions were lifted, the pipeline might not be built because the foreign-flag supertankers then coming into use could deliver foreign oil and refined products to the U.S. Northeast more cheaply than the pipeline could bring refined products from Texas. The Colonial Pipeline was completed in 1963. Automation was then increased aboard Jones Act tankers to reduce crew sizes and improve ships' competitiveness against the pipeline. At about the same time, three maritime strikes on the West Coast induced plans for a West Coast refined products pipeline. In 1965, a pipeline was completed from Puget Sound refineries to Portland, OR.

Today, the Gulf Coast ships approximately 75 million barrels per month of refined products to East Coast states by pipeline. About 15 million barrels per month move to East Coast states by tanker or barge, mostly to Florida, which receives no pipeline service. The East Coast imports about 30 million barrels per month of refined products, about a third from Canada and the rest from Europe, Nigeria, and Venezuela. Meanwhile, the Gulf Coast exports 75 million to 100 million barrels per month of refined products.

On the West Coast, Oregon receives 90% of its refined product from refineries in Puget Sound via pipeline and some from California by vessel. The Gulf Coast ships less than 5 million barrels per month of refined products to California by pipeline and nothing by vessel (via the

Panama Canal). Although California is the third-largest state in terms of refining capacity, it also imports a substantial portion of its refined product needs, mostly from the Pacific Rim, Mexico, and Africa.

Waterborne vs. Railroad Options

For the many refineries located on the coasts, the cost of rail versus vessel transport is particularly relevant. Phillips 66 has chartered two Jones Act product tankers to move crude oil from Eagle Ford, TX, to its Bayway refinery in Linden, NJ (in proximity to New York harbor). The company also supplies that refinery with Bakken oil via railroad (or rail to barge via the Port of Albany), as well as with imported oil from West Africa.[60] The refinery has a capacity of 238,000 barrels per day.

Rail and coastal transport are competitors in supplying crude oil to the coastal refineries that process similar types of crude. Vessels, especially tankers, have superior economics in moving crude, which is why so many refineries are located on the water. A 330,000-barrel tank ship can move the equivalent of four to five unit trains of oil. A larger tanker, of the size used in the Alaska trade, can move the equivalent of 15 unit trains. With the median capacity for U.S. refineries of about 160,000 barrels per day, even the smallest tankers can carry a two-day supply of oil. Rail loading and unloading terminals are being built to accommodate four to five trains per day to match a refinery's delivery needs; the challenge has been developing high-speed pumping equipment that can load/unload an entire train (100 to 120 tank cars) in sufficient time to avoid train backups at terminals (a unit train is over a mile long). On the other hand, coastal refineries already have docks and pumping facilities to receive vessels. Moreover, railroads must build and maintain track and pay property taxes on their rights of way, whereas the cost of building and maintaining navigation channels in harbors is largely born by the federal government. For these reasons, tanker should be significantly cheaper than rail for transport of crude oil, even when the water route is much longer.

A round-trip voyage from the Gulf to the Northeast might take two weeks. Thus, to sustain a supply chain for one refinery, a fleet of several tankers would be needed. As Jones Act-eligible tankers are in very short supply, however, refineries such as Bayway utilize waterborne transport as a supplement to the more expensive rail option from the Bakken. Phillips 66 has stated that if Jones Act eligible tankers were available, it would run 100,000 barrels a day of Gulf Coast oil to this refinery.[61] In 2013, an average of 22,000 barrels a day of Gulf Coast oil was shipped to all seven U.S. Northeast refineries.[62] By rail, Bayway alone receives 50,000 barrels per day and is completing a rail terminal with capacity to unload 75,000 barrels a day.

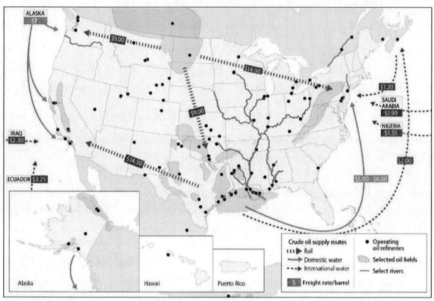

Source: Graphic created by CRS. Map boundaries and information generated using HSIP Gold 2013 – For Official Use Only (Platts); Esri Data & Maps (2013); U.S. Census (2013). Shipping rates approximated from those reported by Turner, Mason & Co. in Platts *Oilgram Price Report*, January-April 2014 issues, and as footnoted in text.

Figure 3. Selected Water and Rail Crude Oil Supply Routes; (Freight rates per barrel).

Eagle Ford crude oil is not currently shipped to California refineries, but such shipments are estimated to cost $14.50 per barrel.[63] The estimated cost of shipping Eagle Ford oil in Jones Act tankers to California through the Panama Canal is $10 per barrel. Again, the water route is cheaper than rail even though the railroad route is only one-fourth the length of the water route. The Panama Canal route would also be cheaper than moving Bakken oil to California refineries via rail to the Pacific Northwest followed by coastwise vessel transport to California, with a total cost of $13 to $14 per barrel.[64] When the Panama Canal's expansion project is completed in 2015, tankers with capacity of 600,000 barrels will be able to pass through, twice the size of the largest tankers using the canal today. This would further increase the cost advantage of ocean transport, if Jones Act-eligible vessels of that size are available.[65]

It is not inconceivable that tankers could also play a role in moving Bakken oil to East or West Coast refineries, although the route would be circuitous compared to rail. Significant amounts of Bakken oil are moved to Gulf Coast terminals by a combination of pipeline, railroad, and barge for refining within that region. From a Gulf Coast port, tankers could transport the oil either to East or West Coast refineries. Existing rail and pipeline connections serve Great Lakes ports, from which tankers could move Bakken oil to Northeast refineries. The experience of agricultural producers in the upper Midwest, however, suggests that these two routing options are not economically feasible because of the Jones Act.[66]

Notwithstanding the U.S.-flag requirement for Alaska oil exports, the situation is somewhat similar to that of Texas oil in that higher domestic shipping rates encourage sales to foreign buyers. This shipping pattern is not unique to oil. In the 1960s and 1970s, the U.S. lumber industry in Washington and Oregon asserted that the Jones Act hindered its ability to compete with western Canadian lumber that could be shipped at cheaper international freight rates to the U.S. east coast.

Today, Oregon and Washington are still large waterborne shippers of forest products, but all their products shipped by water are exported while all the forest products the East Coast receives by vessel are imported.[67] Other bulk shippers have made similar assertions.[68]

Waterborne Transport and Concerns about Rail Safety

If Eagle Ford, and possibly Bakken oil producers were able to access foreign-flag tankers at international rates of around $2 or perhaps less per barrel, some of their domestic oil shipments would likely shift from rail to water.[69] That shift could be beneficial in terms of the safety of oil transport, although the allowance of foreign-flag tankers could potentially displace U.S. seafarer jobs.

Congress is greatly concerned about the safety of shipping crude oil by rail. Existing railroad tank cars are inadequately designed to prevent release of product during derailment, and the transportation of crude oil in unit trains, a new development, has meant that a single incident can involve a large quantity of flammable and explosive material.

Incidents involving unit trains of crude oil have caused numerous fires and explosions, requiring evacuations and in one case resulting in 47 fatalities.[70] Railroads have increased track and equipment inspections on oil routes, and have reduced the speeds of unit trains of crude oil through populated areas. However, recent incidents have shown that a high proportion of derailed tank cars will puncture and release product even at much lower speeds. The capability and resources of local responders to crude-byrail incidents are ongoing concerns.[71]

In contrast, tankers are not a new method for moving oil. Vessels have double hulls and vessel operators are required to have emergency response equipment and resources in place in case of a spill. The Coast Guard has a regulatory regime in place to safeguard tanker transits through harbors. Where allowed, states have imposed additional safeguards on tankers transiting their harbors. Environmental damage from an oil spill remains a grave concern, but tanker incidents generally do not require evacuations of towns and cities.

Impact on Other Rail Users

The heavy reliance on railroads to move crude oil has interfered with the smooth functioning of the rail system. This has had negative consequences for other rail users, including passengers as well as freight shippers.

From 2008 to 2013, annual rail car loadings of crude oil increased from 9,500 to over 400,000.

In 2014, railroads are expected to move 650,000 tank cars of crude oil, the equivalent of 18 unit trains of 100 cars per day.[72] Many of these shipments move out of the Bakken region of North Dakota, and grain, sugar beet, potato, and coal shippers have complained of serious delays in rail service in the Upper Midwest.[73] Amtrak cancelled several trains across North Dakota because the freight railroad that owns the track could not accommodate them, and on other occasions it has had to substitute bus service between points in North Dakota for rail service.[74] Based on past experience, local rail backups can have ramifications for service nationwide.

Some railroads are installing new track to handle the growing demand to ship oil by rail. If tankers were available and their operating costs more competitive with rail costs, it is possible that increased use of waterborne transport could relieve some of the pressure on rail service.[75]

The U.S. Non-contiguous Oil and Gas Trade

The Jones Act is particularly consequential for Puerto Rico, Hawaii, and Alaska. Puerto Rico has no operating refineries. It imports all of its petroleum products. Island countries surrounding Puerto Rico have become major consumers of gasoline and other products refined on the U.S. Gulf

Coast, as has the U.S. Virgin Islands, which is not subject to the Jones Act. However, Puerto Rico does not consume any petroleum products of U.S. origin.[76]

Two refineries located near Honolulu supply about 90% of Hawaii's demand for refined products. Most of the crude oil processed in these refineries comes from Indonesia or other Pacific Rim countries; none comes from other parts of the United States.[77] Any oil or refined products shipped from U.S. ports to Hawaii would have to move on Jones Act ships, putting U.S. production at a cost disadvantage against imports from more distant locations.

New drilling technology has also led to a boom in domestic natural gas production. The gas is cooled to minus 260 degrees Fahrenheit for shipment as liquefied natural gas (LNG) aboard special tankers with insulated tanks. There are no Jones Act-qualified LNG tankers available to carry U.S. natural gas to Hawaii and Puerto Rico; the United States has not built an LNG tanker since 1980. In 2011 (P.L. 112-61), Congress allowed three U.S.-built but foreign-flagged LNG tankers to enter the U.S. domestic trade under U.S. flag, but they have not done so; in any event, these vessels were built in the late 1970s and are over 35 years in age. In 1996 (P.L. 104-324), Congress also allowed any foreign-built or foreign-flagged LNG tankers then operating to re-flag under the United States if they would provide service between a U.S. state and Puerto Rico, but none has entered this service. (These vessels would now be at least 18 years old.) Several LNG export terminals are under development in the continental United States, and these could potentially also handle LNG for Puerto Rico and Hawaii. Puerto Rico has an LNG terminal that receives imported gas, mostly from Trinidad and Tobago, and the potential competitiveness of U.S. LNG shipped in Jones Act vessels is uncertain. Hawaii does not have an LNG terminal.

While Alaskan crude oil exports would be required to move in U.S.-flag tankers, the flag requirement does not apply to LNG. Alaska shipped LNG to Japan in foreign-flag tankers until 2012, and such shipments may resume in the future. Alaska gas could be shipped to the U.S. West Coast if Jones Act-qualified LNG tankers were available.[78]

The U.S. Virgin Islands is exempt from the Jones Act.[79] In the 1960s, Hess built what would become the largest refinery in North America (700,000 barrels per day) at St. Croix. The refinery shipped residual fuel oil to the U.S. East Coast (on foreign-flag tankers). It imported crude oil from foreign sources but also received Alaska oil that sailed around Cape Horn in foreign-flag tankers. In 1976, legislation (S. 2422) was introduced to repeal the Jones Act exemption for crude oil and petroleum products, but no action was taken.[80] The refinery closed in February 2012 and is now used as a storage facility while a buyer is being sought.

Jones Act Waivers

The executive branch has statutory authority to waive the Jones Act "in the interest of national defense."[81] During the summer of 2011, when President Obama released oil from the nation's Strategic Petroleum Reserve (SPR) due to unrest in Libya, the Administration waived the Jones Act and about 25 million barrels of SPR crude oil was moved on foreign-flag tankers to Gulf Coast, East Coast, West Coast, and Hawaii refineries. Each foreign-flag tanker carried 500,000 barrels or more in a total of 44 shipments. One delivery was made in a Jones Act vessel, a barge carrying 150,000 barrels.[82]

The Jones Act has also been waived temporarily after disruptions to normal oil supply routes, in the Gulf after Hurricanes Katrina and Rita in 2005, and in the Northeast after superstorm Sandy in 2012. During the 12-day waiver for superstorm Sandy, 12 foreign-flagged tankers transported more than 3 million barrels of refined product from the Gulf Coast to the Northeast.

RECENT U.S. SHIPBUILDING ACTIVITY

Over the past decade, one tank ship and about 125 tank barges have been built in the United States each year, on average. Limited capacity exists in U.S. shipyards to build tankers. As of February 2014, there were 11 petroleum tankers on order for delivery before 2016 and three ATBs on order.[83] Two of these tankers are definitely being built for crude oil, and are planned to replace two Alaska tankers ready for scrapping. The intended use of the other nine ships has not been announced; they could carry either crude or refined products. If they are intended to carry refined products, the shipyard will install coatings on tank walls and more specialized pumping equipment than needed on crude oil tankers, so that the ship can carry a variety of refined products without cross-contamination.

The tanker ships are being built by the General Dynamics NASSCO Shipyard in San Diego and the Aker Philadelphia Shipyard. One industry analysis estimates that NASSCO has the capability of building four large vessels per year and that Aker has the capability of building three, and that these two yards are essentially booked through at least 2016.[84] Recent ATBs have been built by shipyards in Mississippi, Washington, Oregon, and Pennsylvania.

Foreign Components

NASSCO has partnered with Daewoo Shipbuilding and Aker with Hyundai Mipo Dockyards, both Korean shipbuilders, for ship design, engineering, and procurement support. In the past, shipyard unions have opposed such agreements with Korean shipbuilders because the engines, piping, crew quarters, and portions of the bow and stern were imported from overseas and only assembled in the United States. NASSCO has explained that since Korean yards "build a hundred times more ships, they learn at a rate a hundred times faster, so you learn from the best."[85] Shipyard unions refer to ships built in this manner as "kit ships."[86]

Coast Guard regulations deem a vessel to be U.S. built if (1) all major components of its hull and superstructure are fabricated in the United States, and (2) the vessel is assembled in the United States.[87] The Coast Guard holds that propulsion machinery, other machinery, small engine room equipment modules, consoles, wiring, certain mechanical systems, and outfitting have no bearing on a U.S. build determination.[88]

Shipbuilding Loans, Grants, and Tax Deferrals

The federal government has long provided financial assistance to domestic shipyards. The so-called "Title XI" program (46 U.S.C. §53702) provides government-backed loan guarantees (with repayment over 25 years) for prospective buyers of U.S.-built vessels as well as to shipyards for modernization of their facilities. The loan guarantee covers 87.5% of the cost of a ship. In FY2014, Congress appropriated $38 million for the program, the first time it has provided funds to expand the loan portfolio in several years. For FY2015, the House passed bill (H.R. 4745) would rescind $29 million of this amount while the Senate reported bill (S. 2438) provides $7 million for the program. For each loan, a reserve amount must be held depending on the risk, but typically 5% to 10% of the loan amount. As of April 2014, MARAD had $73 million available for new guarantees, enough to cover approximately $735 million of loans and a current portfolio of outstanding loan guarantees totaling $1.7 billion covering about 250 vessels.[89]

The Title XI program has been controversial in Congress when large loan recipients have defaulted, like in October 2001, when American Classic Voyages defaulted on a loan for two cruise ships intended for the Hawaii trade. Other borrowers have defaulted since.[90] Foreign yards are subsidized also, although the form of assistance is often not transparent. An international agreement to reduce shipbuilding subsidies failed largely because the six largest U.S. shipyards objected to reducing the Title XI program.[91]

In the National Defense Authorization Act for FY2006 (P.L. 109-163, §3506), Congress created a grant program for small shipyards (currently defined as having no more than 1,200 employees). The grant can cover up to 75% of the cost of improving their facilities. Since then, about $10-$15 million a year has been made available for this program, except that the American Recovery and Reinvestment Act of 2009 provided $100 million and no funds were appropriated in FY2014.

MARAD also administers the Capital Construction Fund (CCF) program, which allows U.S.-flag operators to defer taxes on income placed in such a fund if used to purchase or reconstruct U.S. built ships.[92] The fund is established by the ship owner subject to MARAD regulations and reporting requirements.[93] The investment income in the CCF is also tax deferred. The tax deferral is essentially indefinite as long as the program remains active.

U.S.-FLAG RESERVATION FOR EXPORT OF OIL AND NATURAL GAS?

Congress is debating whether to allow crude oil produced in the continental United States to be exported to other countries, in addition to Canada.[94] Domestic producers of natural gas are seeking federal export permits.[95] Current law would not require that such exports be carried in U.S.-flagged ships.[96] Many U.S.-based petroleum producers and refiners control foreign-flag tankers, some of which deliver imported crude oil to the United States or export refined petroleum products from U.S. refineries. U.S. merchant mariners are seeking additional U.S.-flag voyages because the government-impelled cargos (military and food-aid cargos) they rely on are in decline.

During markup of the Coast Guard and Maritime Transportation Act of 2014 (H.R. 4005) an amendment to require that LNG exports move in U.S.-crewed and eventually in U.S.-built tankers was withdrawn in favor of a Government Accountability Office study of maritime employment related to this requirement.[97] Also unsuccessful were two amendments to a House-passed energy bill (H.R. 6, passed on June 25, 2014) which sought to require that LNG exports be carried in U.S.-flag tankers and require that federal regulators give priority to export terminal projects that would use U.S.-flag vessels.[98] Amendments to the Energy and Water Appropriations Act of 2015 (H.R. 4923) would have tied federal approval of LNG export terminals to the use of U.S.-flag tankers, but they were defeated on points of order.[99]

Whether the nation's energy trade should be carried in U.S.-flag tankers is a long-standing debate in Congress. In 2006, when the United States was still expected to be an importer rather than an exporter of LNG, Congress specified that federal regulators give "top priority" to the processing of licenses for offshore LNG import terminals if they would be supplied by U.S.-flag tankers, so as to promote the security of the United States.[100] LNG shippers contended that tying U.S. trade routes to certain flag vessels would hinder the ability to supply LNG under short-term contracts, which was how LNG was increasingly traded as the global market matured.[101]

Security was the rationale put forth by proponents of requiring U.S. imported oil to be carried in U.S.-flag tankers in the 1970s. In 1974, The Energy Transportation Security Act (ETSA, H.R. 8193, 93rd Congress) would have required that 30% of imported oil be carried in U.S.-flag and U.S.-built tankers. The bill was pocket-vetoed by President Ford. In the 94th Congress (1975), Congress created the Strategic Petroleum Reserve in response to the supply crisis in imported oil (P.L. 94-163). Since the oil for the reserve is purchased by the federal government, half the oil shipped by vessel must be transported by U.S.-flag tankers pursuant to the Cargo Preference Act of 1954.[102] In the 95th Congress (1977), the ETSA was reintroduced (H.R. 1037, S. 61) with modifications. A version requiring that 9.5% of U.S. imported oil be carried in U.S.-flag tankers passed the House by voice vote, but was then defeated in a recorded vote of 257 to 165. In the House floor debate, supporters of the bill primarily cited national security and the importance of boosting the domestic shipbuilding base.[103] While opponents cited costs to consumers and potential retaliation from trading partners, much of their argument reflected a Common Cause report on political campaign contributions by the U.S.-flag industry, which had been released just days before.[104] That neither the Department of Defense nor Department of State had testified in support of a national security rationale for the bill was also noted in the floor debate. The Senate never took up the measure.

At a 2014 industry symposium organized by MARAD to solicit ideas for addressing the decline in U.S.-flag cargoes, several participants advocated requiring a certain amount of LNG exports be carried in U.S.-flag or U.S.-built ships.[105] Much of the discussion concerned additional statutory or regulatory requirements for staying the decline in cargoes. There was little or no discussion, given the inverse relationship between price and quantity demanded, of efficiencies that could lower the price of U.S.-flag shipping.[106] The one commercial shipper making a presentation at the symposium stated, "Today U.S. flag is seen as a group of carriers that we have to use. I think that going forward, to be successful, you have to be seen as a group of carriers that we want to use."[107]

CURRENT LEGISLATION

Several bills now pending in Congress address matters related to waterborne transportation of oil, including many of the safety and commercial issues raised in this report:

The Coast Guard and Maritime Transportation Act of 2014 (H.R. 4005, passed by the House April 1, 2014) directs the U.S. Department of Transportation to submit a national maritime strategy that identifies federal regulations that reduce the competitiveness of U.S.-flag vessels in international trade, submit recommendations to make U.S.-flag vessels more competitive and enhance U.S. shipbuilding capability, and identify strategies to increase the use of U.S.-flag vessels to carry imports and exports and domestic commerce. The Coast Guard is directed to arrange with the National Academy of Sciences an assessment of laws that impact the ability of U.S.-flag vessels to compete in international trade, while GAO is directed to study how U.S. maritime employment would be affected by a requirement that LNG exports move in U.S.-flag vessels.

S. 2444, the Coast Guard Authorization Act for Fiscal Years 2015 and 2016, would require the Coast Guard to report marine casualties to state or tribal governments within 24 hours, publish on a publicly accessible website its incident action plans in response to an oil spill, and modify oil spill contingency plans to include advance planning for closing and reopening of fishing grounds.

H.R. 2838, sponsored by Resident Commissioner Pierluisi, would exempt liquefied natural gas and propane tankers serving Puerto Rico from the Jones Act. S. 1483, sponsored by Senator Cantwell, establishes a federal oil spill research committee and requires updates to vessel oil spill response plans.

The National Defense Authorization Act for FY2015 (H.R. 4435), as passed by the House on May 22, 2014, declares the sense of Congress (§3503) that "the United States coastwise trade laws [the Jones Act] promote a strong domestic trade maritime industry, which supports the national security and economic vitality of the United States and the efficient operation of the United States transportation system."

End Notes

[1] For further information on "unconventional" crude oil, see CRS Report R43148, *An Overview of Unconventional Oil and Natural Gas: Resources and Federal Actions*, by Michael Ratner and Mary Tiemann, and CRS Report R42032, *The Bakken Formation: Leading Unconventional Oil Development*, by Michael Ratner et al.

[2] For further analysis on the role of pipelines in moving crude oil, see CRS Report R41668, *Keystone XL Pipeline Project: Key Issues*, by Paul W. Parfomak et al.

[3] See CRS Report R43390, *U.S. Rail Transportation of Crude Oil: Background and Issues for Congress*, by John Frittelli et al.

[4] In this report, barge refers to both a river and a seagoing barge; tanker refers to a deep-draft, self-propelled oceangoing ship; and "tank vessel" refers to both a barge and a tanker.

[5] These factors are discussed in CRS Report R41478, *The U.S. Oil Refining Industry: Background in Changing Markets and Fuel Policies*, by Anthony Andrews et al.

[6] This report focuses on the Coast Guard's role in oil spill prevention. Regarding the agency's role in oil spill response, see CRS Report RL33705, *Oil Spills in U.S. Coastal Waters: Background and Governance*, by Jonathan L. Ramseur.

[7] http://www.portofcorpuschristi.com/index.php/general-information-155/statistics

[8] For further information on these and other routes, see BB&T Capital Markets, "Examining the Crude by Barge Opportunity," June 10, 2013.

[9] A barrel of oil is equal to 42 gallons.

[10] The bow of the tug fits into a notch in the stern of the barge and the tug is hinged to the barge on both sides of its hull, allowing fore and aft (pitch) movement, such as over sea swells.

[11] George H. Reid, *Primer of Towing*, 3rd ed. (Centreville, MD: Cornell Maritime Press, 2004), p. 22.

[12] A unit train consists of only a single type of car, in this case crude oil tank cars, and is not broken up or reconfigured between origin and destination.

[13] Lightering is the process of unloading a portion of an ocean-going tanker's load offshore, or at a harbor's entrance, to reduce the draft of the ship.

[14] Product tankers that carry chemicals are called parcel tankers, and since they have many more and smaller individual holding tanks than petroleum tankers, they would not be practicable for carrying petroleum.

[15] "Shale Oil Has Revolutionized U.S. flagged Oil Tanker Fleet," *Petroleumworld.com*, July 1, 2013.

[16] The News Press, "Supply Shortage Fuels Gas Price Jump," November 21, 2013. According to the article, 97% of Florida's fuel is transported by vessel. The EIA also discusses the tight supply of vessels for transporting Florida's fuel; see, "The Spring Break Travel Rush and Changes in Florida's Gasoline Supply," *This Week in Petroleum*, March 26, 2014.

[17] Washington Analysis, LLC, *Energy Update: Alaska Oil Exports and Jones Act Tankers*, February 27, 2014.

[18] Tankers were identified with assistance from the U.S. Maritime Administration.

[19] U.S. Maritime Administration, *Coastal Tank Vessel Market Snapshot, 2011*, June 2012, p. 2.

[20] Ibid., p. 6.

[21] As per 46 U.S.C. subchapter I. River tows are subject to other regulations in Titles 33 and 46, C.F.R.

[22] NTSB, Recommendation M-99-1. The NTSB is an independent federal agency that investigates accidents in all modes of transportation and makes recommendations on how to improve safety.

[23] 76 *Federal Register* 49976-50050.

[24] See 76 *Federal Register* 49991-49997, August 11, 2011. Crews of towing vessels on the Great Lakes presently use a three-watch system as per 46 U.S.C. §8104(c).

[25] See http://www.regulations, docket no. USCG-2006-24412.

[26] Robert P. Hill, Ocean Tug & Barge Engineering, "The Articulated Tug/Barge – ATB: The History and State of the Art," http://www.oceantugbarge.com/PDF/history

[27] See, Jeff Cowan, "The Articulated Tug Barge (ATB) Quandary," February 13, 2013; Robert P. Hill, "Responding to "The Articulated Tug Barge Quandary," April 5, 2013; and Tom Allegretti, "Safe Operation, Proven Results," April 17, 2013, all at http://www. MarineLink.com.

[28] Navigation Vessel Inspection Circular (NVIC)-2-81, February 25, 1981.

[29] IHS Global Insight, *An Evaluation of Maritime Policy in Meeting the Commercial and Security Needs of the United States*, January 7, 2009, p. 37.

[30] See 78 *Federal Register* 63235, October 23, 2013.

[31] House Committee on Transportation and Infrastructure, Subcommittee on Coast Guard and Maritime Transportation, Hearing on Challenges Facing the Coast Guard's Marine Safety Program, July 27, 2007.

[32] See the 2007 report on the Coast Guard's marine safety mission by a retired Coast Guard vice admiral at http://www.uscg.mil/hq/cg5/cg54/docs/VADM%20Card%20Report.pdf.

[33] U.S. Coast Guard, "Enhancing the Coast Guard's Marine Safety Program," September 25, 2007; http://www.uscg.mil/marinesafetyprogram/. See also *Coast Guard Proceedings*, Summer 2008, pp. 20-28, available at http://www.uscg.mil/proceedings.

[34] http://www.regulations

[35] DHS, Office of Inspector General, "Marine Accident Reporting, Investigations, and Enforcement in the U.S. Coast Guard," OIG-13-92, May 2013; http://www. oig.dhs.gov/assets

[36] This report has been delivered to Congress; http://www.uscg.mil/hq/cg8/cg82/.

[37] The law is codified at Title 46 U.S.C. Chapter 121, Documentation of Vessels (46 U.S.C. §§12101-12152) and Title 46 U.S.C. Chapter 551, Coastwise Trade (46 U.S.C. §§55101-55121).

[38] The Act was named after Senator Wesley L. Jones, Washington State, Chairman of the Senate Interstate and Foreign Commerce Committee, who also included a provision to ensure that

trade between Alaska and the lower 48 states not be shipped through Vancouver, Canada (to the benefit of Seattle).

[39] The ships were sold for about one-tenth the cost of construction. They had high-speed engines and other features that were useful for military operation, but that made them relatively costly to operate in commercial service.

[40] 46 U.S.C. §50101.

[41] *Bloomberg Businessweek*, "U.S. Law Restricting Foreign Ships Leads to Higher Gas Prices," December 12, 2013; *Platts Oilgram News*, "Regulation and Environment," September 9, 2013. See also Senate Committee on Energy and Natural Resources, Testimony of Faisel Khan, Managing Director, Integrated Oil and Gas Research, Citigroup. Hearing to Explore the Effects of Ongoing Changes in Domestic Oil Production, Refining and Distribution on U.S. Gasoline and Fuel Prices, July 16, 2013.

[42] *OilGram Price Report*, McGraw Hill Financial, January-April, 2014.

[43] En*Vantage, Inc., "The Surge in US Crude Oil Production," Presentation to PFAA 20th Annual Conference, October 24, 2013; http://www.pfaa-online.com/docs/2013/AC/8EnVantage-PFAA-Oil-Presentation-102413.pdf.; Bloomberg, "Texas Vies with Saudi Arabian Oil in California Shipments," January 29, 2014.

[44] *OilGram Price Report*, McGraw Hill Financial, January-April 2014 reports.

[45] U.S. Energy Information Administration, Petroleum and Other Liquids, Imports/Exports and Movements, http://www.eia.gov/petroleum

[46] U.S. shipyards have recently been able to export offshore supply vessels (servicing offshore oil platforms), indicating more competitiveness in this category of vessels as well.

[47] U.S. Energy Information Administration, "Additional Information on Jones Act Vessels' Potential Role in Northeast Refinery Closures," May 11, 2012.

[48] U.S. Maritime Administration, *Comparison of U.S. and Foreign-Flag Operating Costs*, September 2011.

[49] U.S. Maritime Administration, *Comparison of U.S. and Foreign-Flag Operating Costs*, September 2011.

[50] U.S. Maritime Administration, *Coastal Tank Vessel Market Snapshot, 2011*, June 2012, p. 6.

[51] Michael D. Tusiani, *The Petroleum Shipping Industry* (Tulsa, OK: PennWell, 1996).

[52] Reuters, "Customs About-face Could Make Bahamas Key Source For U.S. Gasoline," April 23, 2014.

[53] RBN Energy LLC, "Rock The Boat – Don't Rock The Boat – The Jones Act Coastal Trade," January 12, 2014.

[54] RS Platou Economic Research, Monthly Report – May 2014; http://www.platou.com /dnn_site /Default.aspx

[55] Pipeline statistics are available from *Oil and Gas Journal*.

[56] U.S. Army Corps of Engineers, Navigation Data Center; http://www.navigationdatacenter.us/.

[57] A ton-mile is one ton of freight moved one mile.

[58] Association of Oil Pipelines, *Shifts in Petroleum Transportation*, data reproduced by the Bureau of Transportation Statistics, *National Transportation Statistics*, Table 1-61; http://www.rita.dot.gov/bts/sites/rita.dot.gov.bts/files/publications/national_transportation tml.

[59] Federal Trade Commission, Bureau of Economics, *The Petroleum Industry: Mergers, Structural Change, and Antitrust Enforcement*, August 2004, p. 210. A potential decline in the use of heating oil in New England, in favor of natural gas, similarly might affect waterborne and pipeline share in the future because much of the heating oil is carried by barge from New York Harbor.

[60] Phillips 66, Earnings Conference Call, October 30, 2013, Q&A.

[61] Phillips 66 presentation at Bank of America Merrill Lynch Refining Conference, March 6, 2014.

[62] According to EIA, *Crude Oil Movements by Tanker and Barge between PADD Districts*; http://www.eia.gov/dnav/pet/hist/LeafHandler.ashx?n=PET

[63] En*Vantage, Inc., "The Surge in US Crude Oil Production," Presentation to PFAA 20th Annual Conference, October 24, 2013; http://www.pfaa-online.com/docs/2013/AC/8EnVantage-PFAA-Oil-Presentation-102413.pdf

[64] En*Vantage, Inc., "The Surge in US Crude Oil Production," Presentation to PFAA 20th Annual Conference, October 24, 2013; http://www.pfaa-online.com/docs/2013/AC/8EnVantage-PFAA-Oil-Presentation-102413.pdf.

[65] When Alaskan oil began flowing in 1977, West Coast refineries could not handle all the oil. The excess was shipped from Valdez, AK, to Panama on supertankers and transferred there to smaller tankers that could fit through the canal's locks en route to Gulf and East Coast. The high cost of this shipping route ($4 to $5.25 per barrel) led to calls for allowing exports of Alaskan oil to Japan and Korea (with shipping costs of $0.60 per barrel). Later, a pipeline was built across Panama to replace the vessel transit through the Canal.

[66] Grain and feed producers in the upper Midwest contend that while they can move product economically by barge to New Orleans or by rail to a Great Lakes port, from there, because of the Jones Act, they have no economical access to dry bulk ships that could deliver the feed to eastern North Carolina hog and poultry farms. These farms import their feed from Canada and South America, See, for instance, "Can Soybeans Compete?" *Top Producer*, Spring 2005.

[67] U.S. Army Corps of Engineers, Navigation Data Center, http://www.navigationdatacenter.us /wcsc/wcsc.htm.

[68] These include grain and feed, scrap metal, and road salt producers. See U.S. Congress, House Committee on Transportation and Infrastructure, Subcommittee on Coast Guard and Maritime Transportation, *The Impact of U.S. Coastwise Trade Laws on the Transportation System in the United States*, 104th Cong., 2nd sess., 1996, 104-66.

[69] See, for example, the comments of the CEO of Phillips 66 during the company's earnings conference call, July 31, 2013.

[70] For details, see CRS Report R43390, *U.S. Rail Transportation of Crude Oil: Background and Issues for Congress*, by John Frittelli et al.

[71] U.S. Congress, House Committee on Transportation and Infrastructure, Subcommittee on Railroads, Pipelines, and Hazardous Materials, Oversight of Passenger and Freight Rail Safety, 113th Cong., 2nd sess., February 26, 2014; U.S. Congress, Senate Committee on Commerce, Science, and Transportation, Subcommittee on Surface Transportation and Merchant Marine Infrastructure, Safety, and Security, Enhancing Our Rail Safety: Current Challenges for Passenger and Freight Rail, 113th Cong., 2nd sess., March 6, 2014; U.S. Congress, Senate Committee on Appropriations, Subcommittee on Transportation and Housing and Urban Development, and Related Agencies, Rail Safety, 113th Cong., 2nd sess., April 9, 2014.

[72] Platts, *OilGram Price Report*, March 26, 2014, p.1.

[73] "Surge in Rail Shipments of Oil Sidetracks Other Industries; Pileups at BNSF Railway Is Causing Delays for Shippers of Goods Ranging From Coal to Sugar," *The Wall Street Journal*, March 13, 2014.

[74] "Warning: Amtrak Trains Will Not Arrive on Schedule," *Great Falls Tribune*, February 16, 2014.

[75] See, for example, the comments of the CEO of Phillips 66 during the company's earnings conference call, July 31, 2013.

[76] For further information on the Jones Act specific to Puerto Rico, see U.S. Government Accountability Office (GAO), *Puerto Rico: Characteristics of the Island's Maritime Trade and Potential Effects of Modifying the Jones Act*, GAO-13-260, March 2013.

[77] U.S. Energy Information Administration, Geography, U.S. States; http://www.eia.gov/state /?sid=HI.

[78] *Alaska Business Monthly*, "U.S. Cabotage Laws and Alaska's LNG Trade," February 2014.

[79] 46 U.S.C. §55101(b)(4).

[80] U.S. Congress, Senate Committee on Commerce, Subcommittee on Merchant Marine, *Amend the Merchant Marine Act of 1920*, S. 2422, 94th Cong., 2nd sess., February 25, 1976, Serial No. 94-75.

[81] 46 U.S.C. §501.

[82] Staff memorandum to Members, House Committee on Transportation and Infrastructure, Subcommittee on Coast Guard and Maritime Transportation, regarding hearing, "Review of Vessels Used to Carry Strategic Petroleum Reserve Drawdowns," June 22, 2012.

[83] RBN Energy, LLC, "Rock the Boat Don't Rock the Boat – The Jones Act Articulated Barge Fleet," February 11, 2014.

[84] American Petroleum Tanker Partners LP, Form S-1 Registration Statement, October 22, 2013, p. 114.

[85] Tom Wetherald, General Dynamics NASSCO, panel discussion on U.S. shipbuilding at the Second National Maritime Strategy Symposium, hosted by the Maritime Administration, May 6, 2014; http://www.marad.dot.gov/mariners_landing_page/national_strategy_ symposium/National_Maritime_Strategy_Sympo sium.htm.

[86] *Journal of Commerce*, "Unions Sue Over 'Kit' Ships," January 15, 2007; *PR Newswire*, "Metal Trades Department (AFL-CIO) Sues Coast Guard to Block Kit Ships," January 12, 2007.

[87] 49 C.F.R. §67.97.

[88] The Philadelphia Metal Trades Council sued the Coast Guard, but a U.S. District Court sided with the Coast Guard. See *Philadelphia Metal Trades Council v. Allen*, No. 07-145 (E.D. Pa. Jan. 12, 2007).

[89] MARAD, FY2015 Budget Request.

[90] Information on defaults is not available on MARAD's Title XI homepage. On July 14, 2010, the Maritime Administrator at the time testified that since 1993, there had been 13 defaults including two in FY2009 and two in FY2010. Testimony of David Matsuda, House Armed Services Committee on Seapower and Expeditionary Forces, Hearing on Activities of the Maritime Administration, July 14, 2010.

[91] After nearly a decade of receiving no shipbuilding subsidies in the 1980s, U.S. shipyards urged the government to negotiate an international agreement. In 1993, Congress resumed funding for Title XI. In 1994, after five years of negotiations, the United States, the European Union, Norway, Japan, and South Korea reached an agreement through the Organization for Economic Cooperation and Development to prohibit most shipbuilding subsidies. The United States would have been required to reduce Title XI guarantees to 80% of the loan amount and to limit them to 12 years. The so-called "big six" shipyards that do mostly Navy work, but some commercial work, objected to the agreement. The U.S. yards that do mostly commercial work supported it. The United States was the only participant that did not ratify the agreement.

[92] 46 U.S.C. §53501.

[93] 46 C.F.R. Parts 390 and 391.

[94] CRS Report R43442, *U.S. Crude Oil Export Policy: Background and Considerations*, by Phillip Brown et al.

[95] CRS Report R42074, *U.S. Natural Gas Exports: New Opportunities, Uncertain Outcomes*, by Michael Ratner et al.

[96] U.S. law (The Cargo Preference Act) requires 50% of "U.S. government impelled" cargo, such as food-aid, to be shipped in U.S.-flag ships, but these do not have to be U.S. built. Most of these ships also receive operating subsidies because they are to be made available to the military as part of the Maritime Security Fleet program.

[97] H.Rept. 113-384, Howard Coble Coast Guard and Maritime Transportation Act of 2014, p. 27.

[98] *Congressional Record,* June 25, 2014, p. H5750.

[99] H.Amdt. 1029 and H.Amdt. 1031 to H.R. 4923.

[100] P.L. 109-241, §304.

[101] See filings of Shell and the Center for LNG at http://www.regulations under docket no. MARAD-2007-26841.

[102] At the time, the GAO estimated that U.S.-flag shipping costs would be 2.3 to 2.8 times that of foreign-flag rates and questioned whether there was an adequate supply of U.S.-flag tankers. GAO, *Transportation Planning For The Strategic Petroleum Reserve Should Be Improved,* LCD-78-211, October 18, 1978.

[103] *Congressional Record – House,* October 19, 1977, p. 34177 et seq.

[104] "The Maritime Payoff," *Wall Street Journal,* August 4, 1977; "The Great Ship Robbery," *New York Times,* August 6, 1977; "How To Buy A Bill," *The Washington Post,* September 1, 1977.

[105] For webcasts, transcripts and presentations at the symposium, see http://www.marad.dot.gov /mariners_landing_page/national_strategy_symposium/National_Maritime_Strategy_Symp o sium.htm.

[106] This focus is consistent with the observation of a former Maritime Administrator that the U.S. merchant marine has "become accustomed to thinking that the government could never do enough for them." Andrew Gibson and Arthur Donovan, *The Abandoned Ocean* (Columbia, SC: Univ. of South Carolina Press, 2000), p. 175.

[107] Scott Mogavero, Global Logistics and Planning Manager at GE Logistics, as quoted in *Journal of Commerce*, "Shippers Cite U.S.-Flag Challenges," January 15, 2014.

In: Waterborne and Rail Transport of U.S. ...   ISBN: 978-1-63463-003-0
Editor: Patrick Williams   © 2014 Nova Science Publishers, Inc.

Chapter 2

U.S. RAIL TRANSPORTATION OF CRUDE OIL: BACKGROUND AND ISSUES FOR CONGRESS[*]

John Frittelli, Paul W. Parfomak, Jonathan L. Ramseur,
Anthony Andrews, Robert Pirog and Michael Ratner

SUMMARY

North America is experiencing a boom in crude oil supply, primarily due to growing production in the Canadian oil sands and the recent expansion of shale oil production from the Bakken fields in North Dakota and Montana as well as the Eagle Ford and Permian Basins in Texas. Taken together, these new supplies are fundamentally changing the U.S. oil supply-demand balance. The United States now meets 66% of its crude oil demand from production in North America, displacing imports from overseas and positioning the United States to have excess oil and refined products supplies in some regions.

The rapid expansion of North American oil production has led to significant challenges in transporting crudes efficiently and safely to domestic markets—principally refineries—using the nation's legacy pipeline infrastructure. In the face of continued uncertainty about the prospects for additional pipeline capacity, and as a quicker, more flexible alternative to new pipeline projects, North American crude oil producers

---

[*] This is an edited, reformatted and augmented version of a Congressional Research Service publication, No. R43390, dated May 5, 2014.

are increasingly turning to rail as a means of transporting crude supplies to U.S. markets. According to rail industry officials, U.S. freight railroads are estimated to have carried 434,000 carloads of crude oil in 2013 (roughly equivalent to 300 million barrels), compared to 9,500 carloads in 2008. In 2014, 650,000 carloads of crude oil are expected to be carried. Crude imports by rail from Canada have increased more than 20-fold since 2011. The amount of oil transported by rail may also be influenced by a tight market for U.S.-built tankers.

While oil by rail has demonstrated benefits with respect to the efficient movement of oil from producing regions to market hubs, it has also raised significant concerns about transportation safety and potential impacts to the environment. The most recent data available indicate that railroads consistently spill less crude oil per ton-mile transported than other modes of land transportation. Nonetheless, safety and environmental concerns have been underscored by a series of major accidents across North America involving crude oil transportation by rail—including a catastrophic fire that caused numerous fatalities and destroyed much of Lac Mégantic, Quebec, in 2013. Following that event, the U.S. Department of Transportation issued a safety alert warning that the type of crude oil being transported from the Bakken region may be more flammable than traditional heavy crude oil.

Legislation introduced in Congress following the Lac Mégantic disaster would require railroads to have at least two crew members aboard all trains. In addition, policy makers are discussing regulatory changes involving tank car design, prevention of derailments, and selection of preferred routes for transporting oil by rail. Congress may evaluate these changes in the reauthorization of the Rail Safety Improvement Act of 2008 (P.L. 110-432).

INTRODUCTION

North America is experiencing a boom in crude oil supply, primarily due to the growth of heavy crude production in the Canadian oil sands[1] and the recent expansion of shale oil production in North Dakota, Montana, and Texas. North American production now supplies 66% of U.S. crude oil demand, displacing crude from Latin America, Africa, and the Middle East.

This shift has led to significant challenges in transportation, as refineries that once received crude oil principally from oceangoing tankers are now seeing increasing deliveries by domestic transport. Existing pipeline capacity is, in some cases, insufficient to carry growing crude oil from some production areas, or does not link to the refineries needing the oil. The domestic barge network does not serve some key production regions located far from navigable waterways. As a quicker, more flexible alternative to new pipeline projects, North American crude oil producers are increasingly turning to rail as a means of transporting crude supplies to U.S. markets. Increased exports of refined products—and, if Congress changes the law, of crude oil—could lead to even larger volumes of oil being transported by rail. According to rail industry officials, U.S. freight railroads are estimated to have carried 434,000 carloads of crude oil in 2013, or roughly 300 million barrels, compared to 9,500 carloads in 2008.[2] In 2014, 650,000 carloads of crude oil are expected.[3] Crude imports by rail from Canada have increased more than 20-fold since 2011.

The rapid increase in crude oil shipments by rail will likely increase the number of oil spills from rail transportation. However, the most recent data available indicate that railroads consistently spill less crude oil per ton-mile transported than other modes of land transportation. The amount of crude spilled per ton-mile of rail transport declined significantly between the early 1990s and the 2002-2007 period, the most recent years for which data are available.[4]

Nonetheless, the increase in rail shipments of crude has raised safety and environmental concerns. These concerns have been underscored by a series of major incidents involving crude oil transportation by rail, including a catastrophic fire and explosion in Lac Mégantic, Quebec, in July 2013 and a derailment in Casselton, ND, in December 2013 that led to a mass evacuation. Consequently, government agencies in the United States and Canada have issued new regulations and are considering others related to oil transport by rail, and some Members of Congress have called for tighter rules governing crude oil railcars as well as a broader reconsideration of the role of rail in the nation's oil transportation infrastructure.[5]

WHY IS OIL MOVING BY RAIL?

In 2013, the United States produced 2.72 billion barrels of crude oil and imported another 2.82 billion barrels.[6] Canada has become the United States' leading foreign supplier, thanks to its increasing production from oil sands.[7] However, U.S. oil output has been increasing rapidly. In October 2013, U.S crude oil production exceeded imports for the first time since February 1995.[8]

The location of U.S. crude oil production has been changing rapidly. In particular, production in Alaska and from offshore sites has been declining, while production in Texas and North Dakota has been rising. The U.S. Geological Survey recently estimated that 2.7 billion barrels of light sweet crude oil remain in overlooked producing formations,[9] including the Eagle Ford shale, a prolific source of very light sweet crude oil in Texas, and the Bakken formation in North Dakota, a source of light sweet crude oil that rivals West Texas crude in quality.[10]

Almost all oil produced domestically, as well as some Canadian production, flows to one of the 115 U.S. refineries (**Figure 1**).[11] Nearly 45% of the country's refining capacity is located in the Gulf Coast, where 43 refineries process more than 9 million barrels of oil per day (bpd). However, the Midwest and the West Coast also have significant refining capacity.

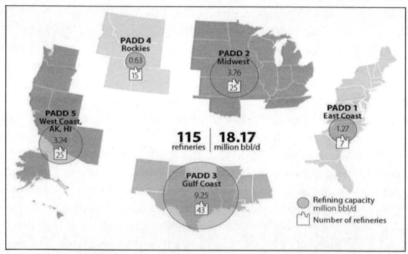

Sources: Congressional Research Service; Energy Information Administration.
Note: PADD = Petroleum Administration for Defense Districts, five districts established by executive order during World War II for gasoline rationing.

Figure 1. U.S. Refinery Capacity by PADD in 2012.

The last entirely new petroleum refinery in the United States opened in 1976. The number of refineries in operation has steadily declined since then as refining capacity has become concentrated in ever larger refineries. A quarter of U.S. capacity is concentrated in 11 refineries with capacities exceeding 300,000 bpd. The largest, Shell/Motiva's Baytown, TX, refinery, was recently expanded to 600,000 bpd. Operable U.S. refining capacity has actually increased from 16.5 million to nearly 18 million bpd over the last decade. Refineries representing approximately 75% of domestic capacity (13.3 million bpd) have the ability to process heavy crude oils, but many smaller refineries can process only light to intermediate crude oil.

Each refinery depends upon a certain grade or blend of crude oils to operate efficiently, depending upon its custom-designed processing equipment. A refinery designed to run light crude oil could not switch to heavy crude oil without adding a coking unit, for example. However some refineries that process heavy sour crude could switch to lighter sweet crude by bypassing their coking units, if the economics of doing so are favorable. Until quite recently, the supply of light sweet crude oil was diminishing, but newly available light sweet crudes from North Dakota's Bakken formation are changing refining dynamics in some regions of the United States, especially as refineries seek supplies that cannot be delivered economically by tanker ships or pipelines.

Traditionally, pipelines and oceangoing tankers have delivered the vast majority of crude to U.S. refineries, accounting for approximately 93% of total receipts (in barrels) in 2012. Although other modes of transportation—rail, barge, and truck—have accounted for a relatively minor portion of crude oil shipments, volumes have been rising very rapidly. The volume of crude oil carried by rail increased 423% between 2011 and 2012, and the volume moving by barge, on inland waterways as well as along intracoastal routes, increased by 53%. The volume of crude oil shipped by truck rose 38% between 2011 and 2012. **Figure 2** shows the change in transportation by mode between 2008 and 2012.

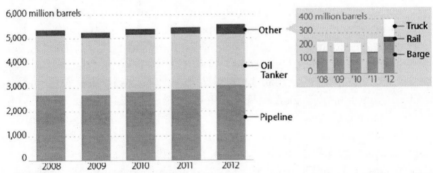

Source: Prepared by CRS; data from EIA, *Refinery Capacity Report*, Table 9, June 2013.

Notes: Some shipments may involve multiple modes, such as rail to barge. This figure indicates only the mode used for the last leg of such shipments.

Figure 2. U.S. Refinery Receipts of Crude Oil by Mode of Transportation.

Rail is a relatively high-cost method of transporting oil. Although crude oil transportation costs are typically not a major driver of refiner profitability, refiners are typically wary of incurring any costs that are higher than those faced by their competitors, as all refined petroleum products sold in a region tend to command the same price independent of the refinery that produced them.

The Economics of Oil by Rail

In the short run, rapid expansion of oil production in the Bakken—production volumes increased nearly ten-fold between 2005 and 2013[12]—strained the capacity of existing pipelines and of refiners able to process the oil. Finding ready buyers was difficult, resulting in discounted prices compared to other crude oil traded in the U.S. market. With Bakken crude selling for approximately $4 to $28 per barrel less than West Texas Intermediate (WTI) crude, the U.S. reference price for crude grade, refiners found it profitable to utilize the North Dakota oil delivered by rail even though the rail transportation cost is perhaps $5 to $10 per barrel higher than pipeline costs.

Rail has also been critical to development of Canadian oil sands. Although the vast majority of crude oil imports from Canada are delivered via existing pipeline, imports by rail are estimated to have increased from 1.6 million barrels in 2011 to 40 million barrels in 2013. Construction of the proposed Keystone XL pipeline could move a significant proportion of these shipments off the rails, as pipeline transportation is likely to cost less per barrel.[13]

For certain refiners, the economics of using rail to transport Bakken oil supplies are even more attractive. In 2012, several refineries in the Philadelphia area were scheduled for closure. The refineries were using imported crudes, largely sourced from West Africa, which sold at a premium to WTI,[14] making their refined products, notably gasoline, uncompetitive against similar products produced by Gulf Coast refineries that used cheaper heavy crudes. By using supplies from the Bakken, these refineries have lowered their costs and have become more competitive. New owners are now investing in the refineries, including installation of high-speed rail unloaders that would allow them to use 230,000 barrels per day of Bakken crude oil by early 2014.[15] These innovations would also reduce the cost of rail transportation per barrel.

The attractiveness of rail transportation of oil may be temporary. Transporting Bakken crude by rail became cost-effective because of the price discounts created by pipeline bottlenecks. If additional oil pipeline capacity were constructed, say from North Dakota to the East Coast market, refiners would likely prefer lower-cost pipeline transportation. And if the refineries could obtain Bakken crude by pipeline, demand would increase, likely reducing or eliminating the current price discount. Without the price discount, Bakken oil would not be competitive in refining when transported by rail. On the other hand, a rising Bakken crude oil price would likely lead to greater drilling activity in the Bakken fields. Given the uncertainty about the future value of the oil and the longevity of the deposits, it is not certain that investors will undertake construction of pipelines from the Bakken fields to the East Coast. In that case, large volumes of crude could be transported by rail well into the future.

Railroads are a viable alternative to pipeline transportation largely because they offer greater flexibility. The nation's railroad network is more geographically extensive than the oil pipeline network, and better able to ship crude oil from new areas of production to North American refineries. While there are about 57,000 miles of crude oil pipeline in the United States, there are nearly 140,000 miles of railroad.[16]

The U.S. Railroad Industry in Brief

The U.S. rail network comprises seven large (Class I) railroads, which focus on moving products between North American regions. These railroads generally market to large volume, long-distance shippers. There are also roughly 500 "shortline" (Class II or III) railroads that sometimes serve as the first or final leg of a Class I rail shipment. Shortlines were often spun-off from Class I railroads because of insufficient business over the line. Class I railroads account for about 70% of system mileage, 90% of railroad employees, and about 95% of freight railroad revenue. Since crude oil movements involve non-traditional rail origins (drilling sites) and destinations (refineries), shortlines are often involved in these movements.

Railroad track is categorized into classes that determine the allowable speeds over the track.[17] Most track with the lowest speed limits is the property of shortlines. If track needs maintenance work, a railroad will issue a "slow order" on that section of track, reducing train speeds.

> Class I railroads have transitioned to using bigger and heavier cars, raising the maximum weight on many track sections from 263,000 lbs. to 286,000 lbs. Shortline railroads that interchange traffic with Class I railroads have had to improve their roadbeds to accommodate the heavier cars.
>
> The railroad industry, since 1980, is mostly economically deregulated. The Surface Transportation Board can review the reasonableness of railroad rates and service in situations where the railroad is determined to have "market dominance," generally where a shipper is served by only one railroad and cannot ship economically by other means. As "common carriers," railroads are required to provide rail service upon reasonable request. Railroads do not require a special federal permit to transport crude oil. Federal railroad law preempts state and local authority, which is generally restricted to a state or local government's "police powers."

The geographic flexibility of the railroad network compared to the oil pipeline network can be especially beneficial for a domestic market in flux. Railroads can increase capacity relatively cheaply and quickly by upgrading tracks and roadbeds to accommodate higher train speeds, building passing sidings or parallel tracks, increasing the frequency of switchovers from one track to the other, and upgrading signal systems to reduce the headway needed between trains. Although railroads need approval from the federal Surface Transportation Board (STB) to build new lines, they do not require STB approval to make improvements to existing lines. And even without capacity improvements, railroads can offer routings not served by pipelines.

A significant fall-off in railroad coal movements has increased railroads' capacity to transport oil over some routes. In 2013, railroads carried about 395,000 more tank cars of crude than in 2005, but about 1.3 million fewer cars of coal. To put the increase in crude traffic in perspective, crude oil represented less than 1% of total rail carloads in 2012. In the first three quarters of 2013, crude carloads increased to 1.4% of total rail car loadings. While, on a national scale, increased rail car loadings of crude oil represent a relatively small percentage of total traffic, significant increases in traffic in a specific area can cause bottlenecks that can reverberate across the entire rail network. The STB held a hearing in April 2014 to hear complaints from non-oil shippers concerning poor rail service in the upper Midwest due to oil traffic and the severe winter weather.[18] The STB ordered BNSF and CP railroads to report how they intended to ensure delivery of fertilizer to farmers in spring

2014. At the hearing, BNSF (the railroad most directly serving the Bakken region) noted that its car loadings in North Dakota had more than doubled from 2009 to 2013, and that in October 2013, crude oil and agricultural car loadings surged by more than it could manage. Past experience has shown that railroad bottlenecks are not quickly resolved.

This experience illustrates that pipelines can generally provide more reliable service than railroads. Among other differences, rail shipments are more affected by weather. In addition, railroads generally experience peak demand during the fall due to the grain harvest and retailers' holiday shipments. This may cause locomotives and track capacity to be in shorter supply at certain times of the year.

Railroad transport reportedly costs in the neighborhood of $10 to $15 per barrel compared with $5 per barrel for pipeline. In return, railroads offer oil producers certain advantages. Heated railroad tank cars improve the viscosity of oil sands crude so that less diluent needs to be added than if the product were being moved by pipeline. Generally, railroads are more willing to enter into shorter-term contracts with shippers than pipelines (1 to 2 years versus 10 to 15 years), offering more flexibility in a rapidly changing oil market. Moving oil by train from North Dakota to the Gulf Coast or Atlantic Coast requires about 5 to 7 days' transit, versus about 40 days for oil moving by pipeline, reducing producers' need for working capital to cover the cost of oil in transit.[19]

Crude oil often moves by unit train, a train that carries just one type of cargo in a single type of car and serving a single destination. Unit trains do not need to be switched or shunted in rail yards, saving time and reducing costs, and return to their point of origin as soon as they have been unloaded. A train consisting of 70 to 120 tank cars can carry in the neighborhood of 50,000 to 90,000 barrels of oil, depending on the type of crude.

One hindrance to the expansion of crude-by-rail has been the lack of tank cars and loading and unloading infrastructure. Much of this investment is being made by the oil industry or by rail equipment leasing companies, not railroads. As of April 2014, manufacturers had 50,000 crude oil tank cars on order, on top of an existing fleet of 43,000. (This is in addition to 30,000 tank cars that carry ethanol and 27,000 that carry other flammable liquids.) In 2013, over 28,000 tank cars of all types were built, up from over 17,000 in 2012.[20] Facilities for building tank cars are unique because the process involves baking the entire car in an oven. One manufacturer believes the tank car builders are capable of increasing production each year by 7,000 to 10,000 cars.

Rail terminal capacity is expected to increase fourfold from 2012 to 2015.[21] Matching the daily throughput volume of a pipeline requires several trains per day, with each train taking 13 to 24 hours to unload; oil rail terminals therefore require large areas for parallel loop tracks where multiple trains can await unloading.

The Role of Barges and Ships in Domestic Crude Transportation

Many refineries traditionally have received crude from overseas and thus are located near the coastline with access to dock facilities. Some are not equipped to receive crude by rail. Hence, some railroads are transferring oil to barges for the last leg of the trip to refineries. Locations where railroads transfer crude oil to barges include St. Louis and Hayti, MO; Osceola, AR; Hennepin, IL; Albany, NY; Yorktown, VA; and Anacortes and Vancouver, WA. In addition, crude produced at Eagle Ford, TX, which is located near ports, is being moved along the coast by either barge or ship.

One river barge can hold 10,000 to 30,000 barrels of oil. Two to three river barges are typically tied together in a single tow that carries 20,000 to 90,000 barrels, about the same load as a unit train. Coastal tank barges designed for open seas, known as articulated tug-barges, or ATBs,[22] can hold 50,000 to 185,000 barrels, although newer ATBs can carry as much as 340,000 barrels, comparable to the capacity of coastal tankers. ATBs are slower, less fuel-efficient, and more restricted by sea conditions, but nevertheless may have an economic advantage over tankers because Coast Guard crewing regulations allow them to sail with one-third to half the crew required on a tanker. Crude oil tankers used to move Alaska oil to West Coast refineries have capacities of 800,000 to over 1 million barrels.

An advantage of tankers over railroads is the greater amount of oil they can carry in a single voyage, which better matches the daily consumption rate of refineries. With the median capacity for U.S. refineries at about 160,000 barrels per day, a coastal tanker can carry a two-day supply of oil. In addition, while railroads must build and maintain tracks and pay property taxes on their rights-of-way, the ocean is free, and harbor channels are largely provided by the federal government. For these reasons, tankers can be much cheaper than railroads in moving oil, even though the railroad route may be much more direct. For instance, the distance between the Bakken region in North Dakota and refineries in the Northeast is approximately 1,800 miles, and the cost of railroad transport is $14 per barrel.[23] The distance from Texas ports near the

Eagle Ford region to the same refineries is about 2,100 miles, and tanker rates are $5 to $6 per barrel.[24] Similarly, the overland distance from the Eagle Ford region to Los Angeles-area refineries is about 1,400 miles, and the estimated cost of railroad transport is $15 per barrel, while the water route through the Panama Canal is 5,200 miles and is estimated to cost $10 per barrel.[25]

Although seemingly a circuitous route compared to rail, it is not inconceivable that tankers could play a role in moving Bakken oil to East or West Coast refineries. Significant amounts of Bakken oil are moved to Gulf Coast terminals by pipeline, railroad, barge, or combinations of these modes for refining within that region. From a Gulf Coast port, tankers could transport the oil to either East or West Coast refineries. Via existing rail and pipeline connections to Great Lakes ports, tankers could also move Bakken oil from there to Northeast refineries. However, the economic viability of these routes, in particular, and routes involving domestic coastal transport in general, is heavily influenced by the Jones Act.[26]

The Jones Act

The Jones Act may have a profound impact on where crude oil is sourced and how it is transported. The Jones Act requires that vessels transporting cargo between two U.S. points be built in the United States, as well as crewed and at least 75% owned by U.S. citizens.[27] The domestic build requirement for tanker ships, in particular, has been identified as contributing to higher costs in moving domestic crude oil along the coasts.[28] Domestically built tankers are about four times the price of foreign-built tankers,[29] and there is limited capacity in U.S. shipyards to build them. Much of the existing crude oil tanker fleet was built since 2000 to meet Oil Pollution Act of 1990 (P.L. 101-380) requirements that tankers calling at U.S. ports have double hulls. Two crude carriers are expected to be delivered in 2014 to replace two vessels in Alaska trade.

As of June 2013, the Jones Act-eligible fleet of crude oil tankers consisted of 10 ships, all employed in moving Alaska crude oil to the U.S. West Coast or to a refinery in Alaska.[30] Since annual Alaska oil production has fallen by about 46% over the last decade, the Jones Act crude oil fleet has been in decline. About 30 Jones Act-eligible tankers carry chemicals or refined petroleum products, such as gasoline or jet fuel, but these ships do not readily alternate between carrying dirty oil (crude oil, residual fuel oil, asphalt) and refined (clean) petroleum products because the tanks would have to be extensively washed after carrying dirty product, a time-consuming and costly process. Some product vessels have fundamentally different designs from crude carriers and would require a layup in a shipyard to be converted to move crude oil.

Phillips 66 has chartered two Jones Act tankers to move crude oil from Eagle Ford, TX, to a refinery in Linden, NJ (in proximity to New York Harbor).[31] Phillips 66 has stated that if more Jones Act-eligible tankers were available, it would like to receive 100,000 barrels a day of Eagle Ford oil at this refinery (it would need several tankers to accomplish this, the exact number depending on the size of the tankers).[32] EIA data (which specify oil movement only between regions, not to individual refineries) indicate that over 13 months from January 2013 to the end of January 2014, an average of 22,000 barrels a day of Texas oil (8.5 million barrels total) were shipped by vessel to all U.S. Northeast refineries.[33] Meanwhile, over the same 13 months, twice as much Texas oil (17.1 million barrels) was shipped to refineries in eastern Canada, in foreign-flag tankers. The oil shipments from Texas to Canada cost approximately $2 per barrel, compared with $5 to $6 per barrel for shipments from Texas to U.S. Northeast refineries in Jones Act-qualified tankers. The cost difference for a 300,000-barrel tanker amounts to around $1 million, meaning that a Texas oil producer receives $1 million less for its oil when shipping to U.S. Northeast refineries than when shipping to Canadian refineries.[34] The Bayway refinery also receives 50,000 barrels of Bakken oil per day by rail, and is finishing construction of a rail unloading terminal with capacity of 75,000 barrels per day. The refinery has a capacity of 238,000 barrels per day. Its remaining sources of oil may be offshore oil from eastern Canada (with shipping rates fluctuating around $1.20 per barrel) and Nigeria (with shipping rates around $1.60 per barrel), as EIA data indicate these were the top two sources of foreign oil for Northeast refineries in 2013.[35]

The Role of Tank Trucks

Tank trucks operating on U.S. roadways have been an important link in moving crude oil from domestic drilling sites to pipelines and rail terminals. A typical tank truck can hold 200 to 250 barrels of crude oil. Trucks readily serve the need for gathering product, as the hydraulic fracturing method of drilling employed in tight oil production involves multiple drilling sites in an area and the location of active wells is constantly in flux. A large volume of crude oil is being transported by truck between production areas and refineries in Texas because of the close proximity of the two.

OIL SPILL CONCERNS

Each mode of oil transportation—pipelines, vessels, rail, and tanker trucks—involves some risk of oil spills. Over the period 1996-2007, railroads consistently spilled less crude oil per ton-mile than trucks or pipelines. Barges and domestic tanker ships have much lower spillage rates than trains (**Figure 3**). However, the data in **Figure 3** precede the recent dramatic increase in oil transportation by rail.

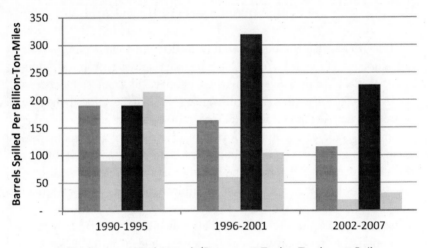

■ Pipelines ■ Tank Vessels/Barges ■ Tanker Trucks ■ Rail

Sources: Prepared by CRS; oil spill volume data from Dagmar Etkin, *Analysis of U.S. Oil Spillage*, API Publication 356, August 2009; ton-mile data from Association of Oil Pipelines, *Report on Shifts in Petroleum Transportation: 1990-2009*, February 2012.

Notes: Pipelines include onshore and offshore pipelines. The time periods were chosen based on the available annual data for both spill volume and ton-miles. The values for each time period are averages of annual data for each six-year period.

Figure 3. Oil Spill Volume per Billion-Ton-Miles; Crude Oil and Petroleum Products during Domestic Transportation.

Given the comparatively small capacity of a rail tank car, around 700 barrels, the total amount spilled from even a major derailment is likely to be small compared to the 260,000 barrels discharged in the 1989 grounding of the *Exxon Valdez* in Prince William Sound, AK, or the approximately 40,000 barrels discharged in the largest U.S. pipeline oil spill CRS can document, which occurred in 1991 near Grand Rapids, MN.[36] Nonetheless, spill volume is arguably a relatively unimportant factor in terms of impacts and cleanup costs. Location matters more: a major spill away from shore will likely cost considerably less to abate than a minor spill in a populated location or sensitive ecosystem. Depending on timing and location, even a small spill can cause significant harm to individual organisms and entire populations.[37]

Although spillage per ton-mile of oil transported by rail declined over time, a recent series of major accidents (see the text box) has heightened concern about the risks involved in shipping crude by rail.

Oil by Rail Derailments in 2013 and 2014

Lac Mégantic, Quebec—On July 5, 2013, a train with 72 loaded tank cars of crude oil from North Dakota moving from Montreal, Quebec, to St. John, New Brunswick, stopped at Nantes, Quebec, at 11:00 pm. The operator and sole railroad employee aboard the train secured it and departed, leaving the train on shortline track with a descending grade of about 1.2%. At about 1:00 AM, it appears the train began rolling down the descending grade toward the town of Lac-Mégantic, about 30 miles from the U.S. border. Near the center of town, 63 tank cars derailed, resulting in multiple explosions and subsequent fires. There were 47 fatalities and extensive damage to the town. 2,000 people were evacuated. The initial determination was that the braking force applied to the train was insufficient to hold it on the 1.2% grade and that the crude oil released was more volatile than expected.

Gainford, Alberta—On October 19, 2013, nine tank cars of propane and four tank cars of crude oil from Canada derailed as a Canadian National train was entering a siding at 22 miles per hour. About 100 residents were evacuated. Three of the propane cars burned, but the tank cars carrying oil were pushed away and did not burn. No one was injured or killed. The cause of the derailment is under investigation.

Aliceville, Alabama—On November 8, 2013, a train hauling 90 cars of crude oil from North Dakota to a refinery near Mobile, AL, derailed on a section of track through a wetland near Aliceville, AL. Thirty tank cars derailed and some dozen of these burned. No one was injured or killed. The derailment occurred on a shortline railroad's track that had been inspected a few days earlier. The train was travelling under the speed limit for this track. The cause of the derailment is under investigation.

Casselton, North Dakota—On December 30, 2013, an eastbound BNSF Railway train hauling 106 tank cars of crude oil struck a westbound train carrying grain that shortly before had derailed onto the eastbound track. Some 34 cars from both trains derailed, including 20 cars carrying crude, which exploded and burned for over 24 hours. About 1,400 residents of Casselton were evacuated but no injuries were reported. The cause of the derailments and subsequent fire is under investigation.

Plaster Rock, New Brunswick—On January 7, 2014, 17 cars of a mixed train hauling crude oil, propane, and other goods derailed likely due to a sudden wheel or axle failure. Five tank cars carrying crude oil caught fire and exploded. The train reportedly was delivering crude from Manitoba and Alberta to the Irving Oil refinery in Saint John, New Brunswick. About 45 homes were evacuated but no injuries were reported.

Philadelphia, Pennsylvania—On January 20, 2014, 7 cars of a 101-car CSX train, including 6 carrying crude oil, derailed on a bridge over the Schuylkill River. No injuries and no leakage were reported, but press photographs showed two cars, one a tanker, leaning over the river.

Vandergrift, Pennsylvania—On February 13, 2014, 21 tank cars of a 120-car train derailed outside Pittsburgh. Nineteen of the derailed cars were carrying crude oil from western Canada, and four of them released product. There was no fire or injuries.

Lynchburg, Virginia—On April 30, 2014, 15 cars in a crude oil train derailed in the downtown area of this city. Three cars caught fire, and some cars derailed into a river along the tracks. The immediate area surrounding the derailment was evacuated. No injuries were reported.

In March and April 2013, there were two derailments of Canadian Pacific trains, one in western Minnesota and the other in Ontario, Canada; less than a tank car of oil leaked in each derailment and neither incident caused a fire.

The increasing deployment of unit trains changes the risks involved in shipping oil by rail in two ways. Unit trains of crude oil concentrate a large amount of potentially environmentally harmful and flammable material, increasing the probability that, should an accident occur, large fires and explosions could result. This risk is similar to that of unit trains carrying ethanol, and maybe greater than that of mixed freight trains in which various hazardous materials, such as explosives and toxic-by-inhalation materials, are sequenced among other cars according to federal regulations.[38] On the other hand, while unit trains concentrate a voluminous quantity of potentially dangerous material, they may offer safety benefits from avoiding the decoupling and re-coupling of cars in rail yards, which involve high-impact forces and introduce opportunity for human error.

Special Concerns About Canadian Dilbit

Oil companies generate substantial quantities of crude oil and related substances from the natural bitumen in oil sands, particularly deposits in Alberta, Canada. In 2012, the United States imported 438 million barrels of oil sands-derived crude oils, 125% more than in 2005.[39] Because bitumen is highly viscous, it is transported mostly in the form of diluted bitumen, or dilbit, containing naptha or other materials that make it flow more easily.

Some commenters have argued that due to its physical characteristics, dilbit presents greater risks of oil spills than conventional crude, with potentially greater impacts to the environment.[40] Other stakeholders and organizations have questioned these conclusions.[41] A study released by the National Research Council in 2013, conducted at the direction of Congress,[42] found that the characteristics of dilbit do not increase the likelihood of spills.[43] The extent to which these findings are applicable to rail transport of crude is open to debate, as rail tanker cars may have different operating parameters (e.g., temperature) and physical standards (e.g., wall thickness), or may transport different forms of oil sands-derived crude oil, decreasing the relevance of the NRC findings.

However, observations in the aftermath of a 2010 pipeline spill are consistent with the assertion that dilbit may pose different hazards, and possibly different risks, than other forms of crude oil. On July 26, 2010, a pipeline owned by Enbridge Inc. released approximately 850,000 gallons of dilbit into Talmadge Creek, a waterway that flows into the Kalamazoo River in Michigan.[44] Three years after the spill, response activities continued,[45] because, according to EPA, the oil sands crude "will not appreciably biodegrade."[46] The dilbit sank to the river bottom, where it mixed with sediment, and EPA has ordered Enbridge to dredge the river to remove the oiled sediment.[47] As a result of this order, Enbridge estimated in September 2013 its response costs would be approximately $1.035 billion,[48] which is substantially higher than the average cost of cleaning up a similar amount of conventional oil.[49]

Special Concerns About Bakken Crude

The properties of Bakken shale oil are highly variable, even within the same oil field. In general, however, Bakken crude oil is much more volatile than other types of crude.[50] Its higher volatility may have important safety implications.

In January 2014, the Pipeline and Hazardous Materials Safety Administration (PHMSA) within the U.S. Department of Transportation (DOT) issued a safety alert warning that recent derailments and resulting fires indicate that crude oil being transported from the Bakken region may be more flammable than traditional heavy crude oil.[51] PHMSA, whose rules are enforced by the Federal Railroad Administration with respect to railroads, reinforced the requirement to properly test, characterize, classify, and where appropriate sufficiently degasify hazardous materials prior to and during transportation. Under its initiative "Operation Classification," PHMSA is to continue to collect samples and measure the characteristics of Bakken crude as well as oil from other locations.

FEDERAL OVERSIGHT OF OIL TRANSPORT BY RAIL

The Federal Railroad Administration (FRA) has jurisdiction over railroad safety. It has about 400 federal inspectors throughout the country and also utilizes state railroad safety inspectors. State inspectors predominantly enforce federal requirements because federal rail safety law preempts state law, and federal law is pervasive. The FRA uses past incident data to determine where its inspection activity should be targeted, although the FRA Administrator stated that in light of the growth of crude-by-rail transportation, the agency also must look for "pockets of risk."[52] FRA regulations cover the safety of track, grade crossings, rail equipment, operating practices, and movement of hazardous materials (hazmat). The Pipeline and Hazardous Materials Safety Administration within DOT (PHMSA) issues requirements for the safe transport of hazmat by all modes of transportation, which the FRA enforces with respect to railroads.[53]

Rail incidents are investigated by the National Transportation Safety Board (NTSB), an independent federal agency. The NTSB makes recommendations toward preventing future incidents based on its findings.[54] Unlike the FRA, the NTSB is not required to weigh the costs against the benefits when considering additional safety measures and it has no regulatory authority. Many of the NTSB's recommendations concerning oil transport by rail are identical to those it previously issued for transporting ethanol by rail. While the FRA has largely agreed with NTSB's recommendations, its rulemaking process involves consultation with industry advisory committees, and it must determine which of the many rail safety measures under evaluation deserve priority. Implementing a change in FRA regulations can take years.

U.S. safety requirements apply to any train operating in the United States, regardless of its origin or destination. Canadian safety regulations are very similar but do not exactly mirror U.S. requirements. Cross-border shipments must meet the requirements of both countries. Safety standards established by the rail industry, which often exceed government requirements, apply to both U.S. and Canadian railroads.

When a rail incident results in the release of oil, state, territorial, or local officials are typically the first government representatives to arrive at the scene and initiate immediate safety measures to protect the public. The National Oil and Hazardous Substances Pollution Contingency Plan, often referred to as the National Contingency Plan (NCP), indicates that state, territorial, or local officials may be responsible for conducting evacuations of affected populations. These first responders also may notify the National Response Center to elevate an incident for federal involvement, at which point the coordinating framework of the NCP would be applied.

Unlike most federal emergency response plans, which are administrative mechanisms, the NCP is codified in federal regulation and is binding and enforceable.[55] The NCP regulations apply to applicable spills from vessels, pipelines, onshore facilities, and offshore facilities. The definition of "onshore facility" includes, but is not limited to "motor vehicles and rolling stock."[56]

If an oil discharge affects navigable waterways, shorelines, or "natural resources belonging to, appertaining to, or under the exclusive management authority of the United States,"[57] Section 311 of the Clean Water Act, as amended by the Oil Pollution Act of 1990, Section 311(c), provides explicit federal authority to respond.[58] The term "discharge" is defined broadly and is not linked to specific sources of oil. The President has the authority to perform cleanup immediately using federal resources, monitor the response efforts of the spiller, or direct the spiller's cleanup activities.[59] Several executive orders have delegated the President's response authority to the Environmental Protection Agency (EPA) within the "inland zone" and to the U.S. Coast Guard within the coastal zone, unless the two agencies agree otherwise.[60] The lead federal agency serves as the On-Scene Coordinator to direct the federal resources used in a federal response.

Regulations require that railroads have either a so-called "basic" response plan or a more "comprehensive" response plan, depending on the volume capacity of the rail car transporting the oil.[61] Comprehensive plans are subject to FRA approval, and must ensure by contract or other means that personnel and equipment are able to handle a worst-case discharge.[62] However, the regulatory threshold for the comprehensive response plan is a tank car holding more than 1,000 barrels, so does not apply to the DOT-111 tank cars used today, which hold around 700 barrels of oil apiece. For these smaller tank cars, railroads must prepare only "basic" response plans, which are not subject to FRA approval.

This threshold was established in 1996,[63] before the advent of oil unit trains, each of which may transport, in aggregate, approximately 70,000 barrels (almost 3 million gallons) of oil. The NTSB recently recommended that the threshold for comprehensive plans be lowered to take into account the use of unit trains.[64]

ISSUES FOR CONGRESS

While oil by rail has demonstrated benefits with respect to the efficient movement of oil from producing regions to market hubs, the dramatic increase in oil by rail shipments has generated interest in several related issues. These include railroad safety,[65] environmental concerns, and trade-offs over rail versus pipeline development.

Railroad Safety and Incident Response

Prior to the Lac Mégantic derailment, the FRA had increased its inspection activity with regard to trains carrying crude oil. After the derailment, the FRA and PHMSA (along with Transport Canada) initiated a comprehensive review of safety requirements.[66] Three areas of active discussion involve tank car design, prevention of derailments, and railroad operations. Railroads are an integrated system of fixed infrastructure, rolling equipment, and workers. Railroad safety experts note that improving safety performance requires recognition of the parameters and interactive effects among these components, and thus approaching railroad safety as an optimization problem is appropriate.[67] For instance, each additional safety feature on tank cars may increase their weight. This reduces the amount of product carried in each car due to track and bridge weight limits, potentially requiring additional tank cars to carry the same amount of product, and thus increasing the expected number of accidents.

In February 2014, the U.S. DOT reached an agreement with railroads under which they would voluntarily take measures to improve the safety of oil trains.[68] These measures include adding braking power; reducing train speeds to 40 mph through urban areas starting July 1 for trains with at least 20 tank cars of crude oil and at least one tank car of the older DOT-111 standard; installing additional wayside wheel bearing detectors by July 1; and other actions. Some of the measures the railroads agreed to are similar to those that the industry already takes for trains carrying "toxic-by-inhalation" hazardous materials. Reducing train speed can reduce the number of cars that derail, as well as the likelihood that product will be released from those tank cars.[69]

Tank Car Safety Design
The U.S. DOT establishes construction standards for tank cars.[70] A tank car used for oil transport is roughly 60 feet long, about 11 feet wide, and 16 feet high (see **Figure 4**). It weighs 80,000 pounds empty and 286,000 pounds when full. It can hold about 30,000 gallons or 715 barrels of oil, depending on the oil's density. The tank is made of steel plate, 7/16 of an inch thick (see 49 C.F.R. §179.201).[71] An oil tank car is typically loaded from the top valve and unloaded from the bottom valve. Loading or unloading each car may take several hours, but multiple cars in a train can be loaded or unloaded simultaneously.

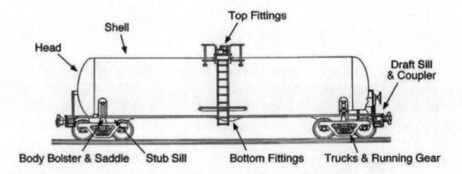

Figure 4. Non-jacketed, Non-pressure Tank Car.

In some incidents, oil has been released from tank cars because the coupler from a neighboring car punctured the tank during derailment. Valves at the top and bottom of the cars have also been sheared off or otherwise opened during derailment. Efforts to improve crashworthiness have focused on reinforcing the shells of tank cars at both ends and/or along the sides with a "jacket" of steel, adding protective head shields at both ends, modifying couplers to prevent decoupling, adding skid protection or diversion shields to protruding valves and modifying pressure relief valves, eliminating or modifying bottom valves so that handles break off rather than opening the valve during derailment, and increasing insulation for fire protection.[72]

The FRA and PHMSA have questioned whether Bakken crude oil, given its characteristics, would more properly be carried in tank cars that have additional safety features, such as those found on pressurized tank cars used for hauling explosive liquids.[73] The railroad industry established additional standards in October 2011 for newly built cars that address some but not all of the safety features that the FRA and PHMSA are considering.

Rail cars have an economic life of 30 to 40 years, so conversion of the fleet to a new car standard could take some time. DOT has asked for further information on the costs and benefits of retrofitting the existing fleet.[74] In November 2013, the Association of American Railroads stated it supports either retrofitting or phasing out oil tank cars built before October 2011 (a fleet of about 78,000 cars) and modifying those built after October 2011 (about 14,000 cars).[75] Some Members of Congress have urged DOT to expedite the rulemaking process concerning new tank car safety requirements.[76]

In February 2014, BNSF announced that it would purchase 5,000 tank cars with safety features that surpass those specified in the October 2011 industry standard (shell thickness would be 9/16 of an inch thick, and they would be jacketed). In April 2014, Transport Canada announced that the oldest DOT-111 tank cars (about 5,000 that lack bottom reinforcement) would no longer be allowed for use in transporting dangerous goods, and the remaining fleet would either be phased out or retrofitted within three years.[77] Transport Canada expects to finalize regulations by the summer of 2014. Reportedly, the U.S. DOT submitted its proposed regulations on tank car safety design to the Office of Management and Budget for review at the end of April 2014.[78] Final U.S. regulations are expected in the summer of 2014, and expected to be in harmony with Canadian regulations. Railroads, shippers, and tank car builders could issue their own standard, but they have not reached agreement on all safety features to be required.

Preventing Derailments

An analysis of freight train derailments from 2001 to 2010 on Class I railroads' mainline track found that broken rails or track welds were the leading cause of derailments, by far.[79] These problems caused 670 derailments over the period, while the next leading problem (track geometry defects) caused just over 300 derailments. Broken rails or welds also resulted in more severe incidents, derailing an average of 13 railroad cars instead of 8.6 cars for all other causes. Broken rails or welds accounted for 23% of total cars derailed. A separate study covering the same time period found that track problems were the most important causes of derailments, followed by problems with train equipment.[80]

In the Rail Safety Improvement Act of 2008 (P.L. 110-432, Section 403(a)), Congress requested that the FRA study and consider revising the frequency and methods of track inspection. The FRA conducted the study and on January 24, 2014 issued a final rule on improving rail integrity.[81] The new rule requires railroads to achieve a specified track failure rate rather than scheduling inspections based on the calendar or traffic volume. It also allows railroads to maximize use of rail inspection vehicle time by prioritizing remedial action when track defects are detected. While the rule requires railroads to achieve a lower track failure rate for track that has higher speed limits, or carries passengers or hazardous material, it does not require lower failure rates for track travelling through populated areas or otherwise consider the affected area around the track in the event of a derailment.[82]

The final rule states that it "codifies standard industry good practices," and notes that railroads "were already initiating and implementing the development of a performance-based risk management concept for determination of rail inspection frequency," meaning that railroads generally have been testing more frequently than required.[83] Large railroads divide their network into hundreds of segments, and determine inspection frequency for each segment based on past inspection results, past history of undetected defects, track tonnage, climate (namely temperature), signaling system (or absence) over segment, whether track carries toxic-byinhalation materials, and whether track is within 500 feet of a structure.[84] They have vehicles to detect defects within the steel of the rail, and others that detect defects in track geometry. From 1980 to 2012, railroads reduced the number of accidents releasing hazmat product per 100,000 hazmat carloads from 14 to 1.[85]

As part of the February 2014 agreement with DOT referenced above, railroads will perform one additional internal-rail inspection each year than required by the FRA on routes over which trains carrying 20 or more tank cars of crude oil travel, and will conduct at least two high-tech track geometry inspections over these routes. Congress may want to look into research on track defect detection technology, including the feasibility of installing equipment on locomotives to achieve near-continuous rail testing.[86]

Shortline Track

It is often the case that a Class I railroad, prior to turning over the operation of a line to a shortline, did not maintain it to the same standards as busier mainlines. Shippers using a shortline often do not require higher-speed track because they ship infrequently or because the commodities they ship are not time-sensitive. Thus, shortline track is frequently maintained at a lower standard than Class I railroads' track. The Lac Mégantic, Quebec, and Aliceville, AL, crude oil derailments occurred on shortline track. Members of Congress have been concerned with preserving shortline rail service, reflected in a federal loan program for track rehabilitation and improvement and a tax credit for shortline track maintenance.[87]

Railroad Operations

A number of specific operational issues have been found relevant to railroad safety, in general, or to oil by rail transportation specifically.

Terminal Operations

In September 2013, the FRA solicited public comment on whether current regulations concerning transfer of crude oil from and to tank cars are adequate considering recent practices at transload facilities. Its request for public comment asked for information about what entity controls trains on loop tracks at rail loading terminals and what procedures have been adopted to prevent unintended movement during loading.[88]

Railroad Crew Size

Following the Lac Mégantic disaster, legislation (H.R. 3040) was introduced in Congress to require two-person crews on all trains. In the United States, the FRA does not specify in regulation how many persons must operate a train, but notes that the various tasks required while a train is moving essentially necessitate at least a two-person crew. Most trains operate with an engineer and a conductor, but some shortline railroads may operate trains with a single crew member. The FRA has announced it intends to issue a proposed rule requiring two-person crews while allowing for some exceptions.[89] One potential trade-off is that distraction by a fellow crew member has been found to be a factor in past accidents.[90]

Positive Train Control

Railroads are in the process of implementing positive train control (PTC), a system that is designed to override human error in controlling the speed and movement of trains. Congress required that this system be installed on routes carrying passengers or poison- or toxic-byinhalation hazardous materials (Section 104 of P.L. 110-432), a requirement that applies to about 60,000 miles of railroad. Current law does not require installation of PTC solely because a track carries crude oil, but the law authorizes the FRA to expand the scope of tracks required to have PTC. PTC is not required on track in or near rail yards. The cost and timeline for implementing PTC are topics of current debate among policy makers and stakeholders.[91]

Route Selection

In the Implementing Recommendations of the 9/11 Commission Act of 2007 (P.L. 110-53, Section 1551), Congress required railroads carrying certain kinds and quantities of potentially dangerous commodities to assess the safest and most secure routes for trains carrying these products and to minimize delays and storage for rail cars containing these products. These requirements currently apply to explosive, toxic-by-inhalation, and radioactive material.[92] Security regulations also require that rail cars containing these commodities not be left unattended when being transferred from one carrier to another or between carrier and shipper.[93] The law resulted from efforts by cities like Washington, DC, and Pittsburgh to ban trains carrying hazardous materials.[94] The FRA may consider whether this routing analysis should also apply to unit trains of crude oil.[95] As part of the February 2014 agreement with DOT mentioned above, railroads agreed to perform this routing analysis for oil trains beginning July 1, 2014. Such a requirement would be controversial because avoiding large urban areas can increase the length of time such trains are in transit and because smaller towns and rural areas likely have less capability to respond to emergencies than large cities. Also, it is unclear to what extent alternative routes are available.

Incident and Oil Spill Response

The increased use of rail for crude oil shipments is likely to increase the number of incidents, some of which may involve oil spills. As described above, the National Oil and Hazardous Substances Contingency Plan provides a framework for federal, state and local collaboration in response to releases of oil and hazardous substances. Considering the relative proximity of rail shipments to population centers, a potential issue for Congress is the safety and adequacy of spill response.

In addition, based on past history, increased frequency or severity of incidents related to shipments of crude oil by rail could lead some local communities to seek additional funding to ensure adequate spill response capabilities, including personnel, training, equipment, and community notification.

The Accuracy of Train Cargo Information

Crude oil may sometimes be carried by "mixed trains"—trains carrying a variety of different commodities. With mixed trains, it is important to first responders that they have an accurate list of which cars contain what commodities (the train "consist"). Often the sequencing of cars changes en route, so the consist information provided by the crew at the scene of an incident may no longer be accurate. Although all vehicles containing hazardous materials must display placards indicating their potential dangerous characteristics (e.g., flammable, corrosive, explosive), responders often need more specific information about the commodities involved in an incident. One potential remedy under consideration is an electronic manifest system that would offer the capability of easier updates. In MAP-21, Congress authorized PHMSA to conduct pilot projects on paperless hazmat information sharing among carriers (of various modes including rail) and first responders.[96] A potential drawback raised by the railroads is that electronic devices at the scene of an incident could encounter technical problems. Another remedy is greater diligence by railroad crew in keeping the paper consist up to date. The NTSB has asked whether a copy of the consist should also be kept at the end of a train in case the copy kept by the crew at the head of the train is lost in an incident.

Rail vs. Pipeline Development

Certain rail routings of crude oil could be replaced by reconfiguring the existing pipeline network and constructing additional pipeline capacity. In general, pipelines could provide safer, less expensive transportation than railroads, assuming that pipeline developers are able to assure markets for the oil they hope to carry.

Pipeline development could be particularly important for shipments of crude oil from Canada to the United States. In light of growing Canadian exports, several proposals have been made to expand the cross-border pipeline infrastructure. Of the five major pipelines currently linking Canadian petroleum producing regions to markets in the United States, two (Alberta Clipper and Keystone) began service in 2010. A permit application for a sixth pipeline, Keystone XL, a very large project which would also transport some Bakken crude, was initially submitted in 2008 and is in the final stages of review by the U.S. Department of State.[97] Keystone XL has been the subject of intense scrutiny and debate by Congress, the executive branch, and numerous stakeholders. The Keystone XL review and approval process is highly contested, and the pipeline's approval remains uncertain.

Other proposed oil pipeline projects, such as the reversal of the Portland-Montreal oil pipeline to enable export of Canadian oil via a marine terminal in Maine, are also encountering greater public scrutiny and opposition. On the whole, the barriers to new oil pipeline approval in any jurisdiction seem to have risen significantly since Alberta Clipper and Keystone were completed.

Shipment of oil by rail is, in many cases, an alternative to new pipeline development. This involves tradeoffs in terms of both transportation capacity and safety. In its ongoing review of the Keystone XL pipeline proposal, the State Department has argued that, if the pipeline is not constructed, additional oil-by-rail capacity will be developed instead. As the State Department's 2014 Final Environmental Impact Statement for the Keystone XL project states,

> In the past 2 years, there has been exponential growth in the use of rail to transport crude oil throughout North America, primarily originating from the Bakken in North Dakota and Montana, but also increasingly utilized in other production areas, including the [Western Canadian Sedimentary Basin]. Because of the flexibility of rail delivery points, once loaded onto trains the crude oil could be delivered to refineries, terminals, and/or port facilities throughout North America, including the Gulf Coast area.[98]

Consistent with this view, both Canadian National Railway and Canadian Pacific Railway reportedly have been pursuing a "pipeline on rails" business strategy, including new track investments, to move Canadian crudes to new markets throughout North America.[99] Increasing cross-border movements of crude oil by rail on existing track does not require State Department approval, so such an approach seeks to avoid regulatory delays. While the potential volumes associated with rail transportation of crude could be lower than pipeline volumes, they could still be significant. Some analysts have suggested that oil-by-rail volumes could be large enough to make a major new pipeline project like Keystone XL unnecessary.[100] Similar arguments could apply to other oil transportation corridors within North America.

Others are less certain that oil by rail can substitute so readily for pipeline capacity, as rail expansion would require significant infrastructure development including loading and unloading facilities, track capacity, and, possibly, additional tank car availability. The State Department's analysis finds that under certain conditions, including particular oil and oil transportation prices, "there could be a substantial impact on oil sands production levels."[101] Other market analyses similarly find that in the short and medium term some production could be curtailed.[102]

Refiner economics may ultimately favor pipelines over rail, although those investment decisions will be determined by market forces. When it comes to safety, however, the federal government plays a major role, and thus may have considerable influence on infrastructure expansion. Some participants in the Keystone XL debate, for example, have asserted that recent oil-by-rail incidents underscore the need for a new pipeline as, in their view, a safer mode of transportation for Canadian crudes,[103] while others insist that safety comparisons between the two transportation modes are less conclusive.[104] On balance, however, it seems likely that policies that raise the cost of transporting oil by rail would increase the attractiveness of pipeline development, and, for that matter, expansion of crude oil transportation by barges, tanker ships, and tanker trucks.

Rail vs. Waterborne Transport

As indicated above, the cost of transporting oil along the coasts in Jones Act tankers is much less than by railroad. However, the fleet of Jones Act-qualified tankers is insufficient to take advantage of this lower-cost shipping method. Despite the domestic oil boom, coastal refineries continue to rely on foreign sources of oil that are shipped at rates generally ranging from less than a dollar per barrel (Mexico to the Gulf Coast) to less than $2.50 a barrel (Saudi Arabia to the Atlantic Coast).[105] In addition to efficient transport, safety is a concern. Tankers are not a new transport method. Tankers are double-hulled, operators are required to have resources and equipment nearby in case of a spill, and the Coast Guard has a regulatory regime in place to promote safe transits through harbors. While the risk of an oil spill in a marine environment remains a grave concern, coastal transport largely avoids travel through towns and cities. The railroads have had difficulty in dealing with the surge in oil traffic, and other rail users are experiencing severe service disruptions in the upper Midwest. An important but open question is whether more oil would be moving by coastwise shipping, relieving some of the safety and capacity pressure on railroads, if tankers were available and their operating costs more competitive. The CEO of Phillips 66 has stated, "I think our view is that because of the limitations on Jones Act vessels, that's going to push you to more barge and more rail, just to evacuate the Gulf Coast."[106]

Rail Transport and Crude Oil Exports

The large increase in U.S. oil production has led some Members of Congress to advocate changing the law that generally prohibits exports of crude oil.[107] An increase in crude oil exports would likely require greater use of rail transportation, as the crude oil pipeline network is not oriented to serve export ports. Some environmental groups have stated their opposition to construction of new rail facilities or terminals that would facilitate oil exports, as they believe increased exports will encourage environmentally damaging production in the United States and Canada.[108]

End Notes

[1] The terms "oil sands" and "tar sands" are often used interchangeably to describe a particular type of nonconventional oil deposit. Opponents of the resource's development often use the term "tar sands," which arguably carries a negative connotation; proponents typically refer to the material as oil sands. The use of this term is not intended to reflect a point of view, but to adopt the term most commonly used by the primary executive-branch agencies involved in recent oil sands policy issues.

[2] Edward R. Hamberger and Andrew J. Black, "Freight Rail and Pipelines Deliver Energy for America," *The Hill, Congress Blog*, November 5, 2013, http://thehill.com/blogs/

[3] *Oilgram Price Report*, "North American Crude By Rail Rising: BNSF," v. 92, no. 58, March 26, 2014, p. 1.

[4] Estimates by CRS based on data from Dagmar Etkin, *Analysis of U.S. Oil Spillage*, API Publication 356, August 2009, and Association of Oil Pipelines, *Report on Shifts in Petroleum Transportation: 1990-2009*, February 2012.

[5] See, for example, Office of Senator John Hoeven, "Hoeven to Meet Saturday with BNSF Railway President and CEO to Address Railroad Safety," press release, January 3, 2014.

[6] Energy Information Administration, *U.S. Crude Oil Supply & Disposition*, http://www.eia.gov/dnav/pet/ pet_sum_crdsnd_k_a.htm. A barrel of oil is equal to 42 gallons.

[7] CRS Report R43128, *Oil Sands and the Oil Spill Liability Trust Fund: The Definition of "Oil" and Related Issues for Congress*, by Jonathan L. Ramseur.

[8] "US Crude Production Tops Imports For The First Time Since 1995," *Oil Daily*, November 14, 2013.

[9] M. Tennyson et al., *Assessment of Remaining Recoverable Oil in Selected Major Oil Fields of the Permian Basin, Texas and New Mexico*, 2012, USGS, http://pubs.usgs.gov/fs/2012/3051/.

[10] "Light" refers to oils with low specific gravity. "Sweet" refers to oils with low sulfur content. Light, sweet crudes are more valuable than heavier or sourer crude oils.

[11] For further information on the petroleum refining industry, refer to CRS Report R41478, *The U.S. Oil Refining Industry: Background in Changing Markets and Fuel Policies*, by Anthony Andrews et al.

[12] Energy Information Administration crude oil production data, by state, available at http://www.eia.doe.gov.

[13] For more information about the Keystone XL pipeline, see CRS Report R41668, *Keystone XL Pipeline Project: Key Issues*, by Paul W. Parfomak et al.

[14] Energy Information Administration price data available at http://www.eia.doe.gov.

[15] Matthew Phillips, "North Dakota's Bakken Oil Finally Hits the East Coast," *Bloomberg Businessweek*, February 6, 2013.

[16] Pipeline data from PHMSA, railroad mileage from Association of American Railroads (includes shortline rail mileage, does not include parallel trackage).

[17] See 49 C.F.R. §213.9.

[18] STB, Docket no. EP 724, April 10, 2004.

[19] BB&T Capital Markets, "Examining The Crude By Barge Opportunity," June 10, 2013, p. 15.

[20] Tank car numbers from presentations by panel on tank car safety (panel 1), NTSB forum, *Rail Safety: Transportation of Crude Oil and Ethanol*, April 22-23, 2014.

[21] E. Russell Braziel, RBN Energy Inc. presentation at CSIS conference, *North American Oil and Gas Infrastructure, Shale Changes Everything*," November 14, 2013.

[22] The bow of the tug fits into a notch in the stern of the barge and the tug is hinged to the barge on both sides of its hull, allowing fore and aft (pitch) movement, such as over sea swells.

[23] Platts, *Oilgram Price Report*, January through April 2014 issues. Railroad distance approximated using Rand McNally Road Atlas.

[24] Platts, *Oilgram News*, September 9, 2013; Bloomberg Businessweek, "U.S. Law Restricting Foreign Ships Leads to Higher Gas Prices," December 12, 2013. The sailing distance is 1,900 nautical miles (one nautical mile equals 1.151 statute miles); National Oceanic and Atmospheric Administration, *Distances Between United States Ports*, 2012.

[25] En*Vantage, Inc., "The Surge in U.S. Crude Oil Production," Presentation to PFAA 20th Annual Conference, October 24, 2013; Bloomberg, "Texas Vies with Saudi Arabian Oil in California Shipments," January 29, 2014. When expansion of the locks through the Panama Canal is completed in 2015, the capacity of tankers able to pass through will increase from 380,000 barrels to 600,000 barrels.

[26] Grain and feed producers in the upper Midwest contend that while they can move product economically by barge to New Orleans or by rail to a Great Lakes port, from there, because of the Jones Act, they have no economic access to dry bulk ships that could deliver the feed

to eastern North Carolina hog and poultry farms. These farms import their feed from Canada and South America.

[27] The law is codified at chapters 81, 121, and 551 of Title 46, *United States Code.*

[28] See for instance, "Oil and the Ghost of 1920," *Wall Street Journal,* September 13, 2012; Senate Committee on Energy and Natural Resources, Testimony of Faisel Khan, Managing Director, Integrated Oil and Gas Research, Citigroup. Hearing to Explore the Effects of Ongoing Changes in Domestic Oil Production, Refining and Distribution on U.S. Gasoline and Fuel Prices, July 16, 2013.

[29] U.S. Maritime Administration, Title XI Ship Financing Guarantees, Pending and Approved Loan Applications; American Petroleum Tankers S-1 SEC Filing; RS Platou Economic Research, annual and monthly reports; press releases from Teekay Tankers, Scorpio Tankers, and Euronav.

[30] U.S. Maritime Administration, U.S. Flag Privately Owned Merchant Fleet, Oceangoing Self-propelled Vessels.

[31] "Phillips 66 Charters Tankers To Bring Shale Oil To Bayway," *Argus Media,* December 13, 2012.

[32] Phillips 66 presentation at Bank of America Merrill Lynch Refining Conference, March 6, 2014.

[33] U.S. Northeast refineries are clustered around New York Harbor and the Delaware River.

[34] This situation is somewhat similar to the Pacific Northwest lumber industry in the 1960s and 1970s, which asserted it could not compete with western Canadian lumber because the Canadians could ship at lower international freight rates to the U.S. East Coast. Washington and Oregon still load significant amounts of wood products on ships, but they all sail to foreign destinations.

[35] Shipping rates from Platts, *Oilgram Price Report,* January through April 2014 issues.

[36] Sources consulted include NOAA, Oil Spill Case Histories, 1967-1991, Summaries of Significant U.S. and International Spills, 1992; U.S. Coast Guard, Notable Spills in U.S. Waters, Calendar Years 1989-2008, 2009; Dagmar Etkin, Analysis of U.S. Oil Spillage, API Publication 356, August 2009; NOAA, Incident News, at http://incidentnews.gov; EPA, Enforcement and Compliance History Online (ECHO), at http://www.epa-echo.gov/echo/index.html.

[37] National Research Council, *Oil in the Sea III: Inputs, Fates, and Effects* (Washington, DC: National Academies of Science, February 2003).

[38] These requirements are codified at 49 CFR §174.85.

[39] Data from Canada's National Energy Board. See also CRS Report R43128, *Oil Sands and the Oil Spill Liability Trust Fund: The Definition of "Oil" and Related Issues for Congress,* by Jonathan L. Ramseur.

[40] The primary vehicle for these arguments was a 2011 report from several environmental groups. See Anthony Swift et al., *Tar Sands Pipelines Safety Risks,* Joint Report by Natural Resources Defense Council, National Wildlife Federation, Pipeline Safety Trust, and Sierra Club, February 2011.

[41] See, e.g., Crude Quality Inc., *Report regarding the U.S. Department of State Supplementary Draft Environmental Impact Statement,* May 2011; and Energy Resources Conservation Board, Press Release, "ERCB Addresses Statements in Natural Resources Defense Council Pipeline Safety Report," February 2011.

[42] P.L. 112-90, §16.

[43] National Research Council, *Effects of Diluted Bitumen on Crude Oil Transmission Pipelines,* 2013.

[44] National Transportation Safety Board, *Accident Report: Enbridge Incorporated Hazardous Liquid Pipeline Rupture and Release- Marshall, Michigan, July 25, 2010*, July 2012, at http://www.ntsb.gov/.

[45] For more up-to-date information, see EPA's Enbridge oil spill website at http://www.epa.gov/enbridgespill/ index.html.

[46] Letter from Cynthia Giles, Environmental Protection Agency, to U.S. Department of State, April 22, 2013.

[47] EPA Removal Order, March 14, 2013, at http://www.epa.gov/enbridgespill/ar/enbridge-AR-1720.pdf.

[48] See Enbridge Inc., Third Quarter Financial Report, 2013, at http://enbridge.com/InvestorRelations/FinancialInformation/InvestorDocumentsandFilings.aspx.

[49] Based on cost estimates prepared in 2004. See Dagmar Etkin, *Modeling Oil Spill Response and Damages Costs*, Proceedings of the 5th Biennial Freshwater Spills Symposium, 2004, at http://www.environmental-research.com.

[50] Bryden, K. J., Grace Catalysts Technologies, Columbia, Maryland; Habib Jr., E. T., Grace Catalysts Technologies, Columbia, Maryland; Topete, O. A., Grace Catalysts Technologies, Houston, Texas, Processing shale oils in FCC: Challenges and opportunities 09.01.2013 http://www.hydrocarbonprocessing.com/Article/3250397/Processing-shaleoils-in-FCC-Challenges-and-opportunities.html.

[51] Pipeline and Hazardous Materials Safety Administration, Safety Alert—January 2, 2014, Preliminary Guidance from OPERATION CLASSIFICATION. This advisory is a follow-up to the PHMSA and Federal Railroad Administration (FRA) joint safety advisory published November 20, 2013 [78 FR 69745].

[52] FRA Administrator Szabo, Opening Remarks to RSAC Meeting, October. 31, 2013; http://www.fra.dot.gov/eLib/ Details/L04852.

[53] FRA and PHMSA are agencies within DOT, which has the emergency authority to restrict or prohibit transportation that poses a hazard of death, personal injury, or significant harm to the environment. See 49 U.S.C. §20104.

[54] The NTSB held a forum on the safety of crude oil and ethanol transport by rail April 22 and 23, 2014; http://www.ntsb.gov/news/events/2014/railsafetyforum/.

[55] 40 C.F.R. Part 112.

[56] 40 C.F.R. §300.5. This definition is also found in the Clean Water Act and OPA.

[57] The Oil Pollution Act of 1990 expanded and clarified the President's authorities under Section 311 of the Clean Water Act (33 U.S.C. §2701 et. seq.). For a more in-depth discussion of the Oil Pollution Act, see CRS Report RL33705, *Oil Spills in U.S. Coastal Waters: Background and Governance*, by Jonathan L. Ramseur.

[58] 33 U.S.C. §1321. In addition, the Comprehensive Environmental Response, Compensation, and Liability Act (CERCLA) of 1980 expanded the authorities of the President to respond to releases of hazardous substances into the environment more broadly than CWA Section 311. See CRS Report R41039, *Comprehensive Environmental Response, Compensation, and Liability Act: A Summary of Superfund Cleanup Authorities and Related Provisions of the Act*, by David M. Bearden. For further details, see CRS Report R43251, *Oil and Chemical Spills: Federal Emergency Response Framework*, by David M. Bearden and Jonathan L. Ramseur.

[59] 33 U.S.C. §1321(c).

[60] Executive Order 12777, "Implementation of Section 311 of the Federal Water Pollution Control Act of October 18, 1972, as amended, and the Oil Pollution Act of 1990," 56 *Federal Register* 54757, October 22, 1991.

[61] 49 C.F.R. Part 130.

[62] See 49 C.F.R. §130.31(a) with 49 C.F.R. §130.31(b).

[63] 61 *Federal Register* 30541 (June 17, 1996).

[64] NTSB, Safety Recommendation R-14-4 through -6, directed to PHMSA, January 21, 2014.

[65] U.S. Congress, House Committee on Transportation and Infrastructure, Subcommittee on Railroads, Pipelines, and Hazardous Materials, *Oversight of Passenger and Freight Rail Safety*, 113th Cong., 2nd sess., February 26, 2014; U.S. Congress, Senate Committee on Commerce, Science, and Transportation, Subcommittee on Surface Transportation and Merchant Marine Infrastructure, Safety, and Security, *Enhancing Our Rail Safety: Current Challenges for Passenger and Freight Rail*, 113th Cong., 2nd sess., March 6, 2014; U.S. Congress, Senate Committee on Appropriations, Subcommittee on Transportation and Housing and Urban Development, and Related Agencies, *Rail Safety*, 113th Cong., 2nd sess., April 9, 2014.

[66] See FRA's Emergency Order No. 28 (78 *Federal Register* 48218), the agencies' Joint Safety Advisory published August 7, 2013 (78 *Federal Register* 48224), referral of safety issues to FRA's Railroad Safety Advisory Committee (78 *Federal Register* 48931), and a NPRM related to rail hazmat (78 *Federal Register* 54849).

[67] Xiang Liu, M. Rapik Saat, Christopher P.L. Barkan, *Safety Effectiveness of Integrated Risk Reduction Strategies for the Transportation of Hazardous Materials by Rail*, paper presented at the Transportation Research Board, Annual Meeting 2013, paper no. 13-1811.

[68] AAR, "Freight Railroads Join U.S. Transportation Secretary Foxx in Announcing Industry Crude By Rail Safety Initiative," February 21, 2014.

[69] Athaphon Kawprasert and Christopher P.L. Barkan, "Effect of Train Speed on Risk Analysis of Transporting Hazardous Materials by Rail," *Transportation Research Record*, No. 2159, 2010, pp. 59-68.

[70] The tank cars used to transport crude oil fall under DOT specification 111. See 49 C.F.R. §179.

[71] 49 C.F.R. §179.201.

[72] For a discussion of NTSB's recommendations concerning DOT-111 tank cars, in reference to the derailment of an ethanol unit train in Cherry Valley, IL, see NTSB Safety Recommendation R-12-5 through -8, March 2, 2012.

[73] Pressurized tank cars (DOT specification 105 and 112) have thicker shells and heads, metal jackets, strong protective housings for top fittings, and no bottom valves.

[74] 78 FR 54849 - 54861, September 6, 2013.

[75] For comments filed on this rulemaking see http://www.regulations and search under docket no. PHMSA-2012- 0082.

[76] See letter from Senator Schumer to PHMSA and FRA dated July 22, 2013 and news release by Senator Hoeven on January 15, 2013 indicating that a DOT final rule on tank cars would not be issued until after January 2015.

[77] Transport Canada, "Addressing the safety of DOT-111 tank cars carrying dangerous goods," April 23, 2014.

[78] CQ News, "Oil Train Regulations Couldn't Come Soon Enough For Some Railroads," May 1, 2014.

[79] T87.6 Task Force Summary Report, pp. 9-11; Xiang Liu, M. Rapik Saat, Christopher P.L. Barkan, "Analysis of Causes of Major Train Derailment and Their Effect on Accident Rates," *Transportation Research Record*, No. 2289, 2012, pp. 154-163.

[80] Xiang Liu, M. Rapik Saat, Christopher P.L. Barkan, *Safety Effectiveness of Integrated Risk Reduction Strategies for the Transportation of Hazardous Materials by Rail*, Paper presented at the Transportation Research Board, Annual Meeting 2013, paper no. 13-1811.

[81] 79 *Federal Register* 4234, January 24, 2014.

[82] This risk element has been studied by Xiang Liu, University of Illinois at Urbana-Champaign—RailTEC, Presentation at Transportation Research Board Annual Meeting, Session 279, *Broken Rail Prevention and Rail Flaw Assessment*, Washington, DC, January 13, 2014.

[83] 79 *Federal Register* 4234 and 4245, January 24, 2014.

[84] Presentations of BNSF and UP Railroads, Transportation Research Board Annual Meeting, Washington, DC, January 13, 2014, Session 279, *Broken Rail Prevention and Rail Flaw Assessment*.

[85] Christopher P.L. Barkan, M. Rapik Saat, and Francisco Gonzalez III et al., "Cooperative Research in Tank Car Safety Design," *TR News*, vol. 286 (May-June 2013), pp. 12-19.

[86] This topic was briefly discussed at the NTSB forum on rail safety cited above.

[87] The Railroad Rehabilitation and Improvement Financing (RRIF) program and Section 45G of the tax code.

[88] "FRA/PHMSA Additional Questions for Public Comment," Docket No. FRA-2013-0067-0016, 9/4/2013, http://www.regulations.

[89] Press Release no. FRA-03-14, April 9, 2014.

[90] NTSB, *Collision of Two CN Freight Trains, Anding, Mississippi, July 10, 2005*, Accident Report RAR-07/01, p. 31.

[91] For further information, see CRS Report R42637, *Positive Train Control (PTC): Overview and Policy Issues*, by John Frittelli.

[92] See 49 C.F.R. §172.820; 73 *Federal Register* 72182, November 26, 2008.

[93] See 49 C.F.R. §1580.107.

[94] *U.S. Rail News*, June 11, 2008, pp. 1-2; "Hazmat Hazards: U.S. Cities may not wait for Washington Before Trying to Reroute their own hazmat trains," *Journal of Commerce*, December 12, 2005.

[95] RSAC meeting, presentation by HAZMAT Working Group, October 31, 2013. The NTSB has recommended this change; see Safety Recommendation R-14-1 through -3, January 23, 2014.

[96] Section 33005 of P.L. 112-141.

[97] The construction, connection, operation, and maintenance of a pipeline connecting the United States with a foreign country require executive permission through a Presidential Permit under Executive Orders 11423 and 13337.

[98] U.S. Department of State, January 2014, Final EIS, Section 5.1, "No Action Alternatives."

[99] Nathan Vanderklippe, "CN, CP Push for a 'Pipeline on Rails,'" *Globe and Mail*, February 7, 2011.

[100] "Keystone Pipeline Seen as Unneeded as More Oil Moves by Rail," *CBC News*, September 10, 2013.

[101] 2014 Final EIS, p. 1.4-8.

[102] For example, Canadian Imperial Bank of Commerce, "Too Much of A Good Thing: A Deep Dive Into The North American Energy Renaissance," August 15, 2012; TD Economics, "Pipeline Expansion is a National Priority," Special Report, December 17, 2012; International Energy Agency," Medium-Term Oil Market Report," May 14, 2013.

[103] Diana Furchtgott-Roth and Kenneth P. Green, *Intermodal Safety in the Transport of Oil*, Fraser Institute, October 2013, http://www.fraserinstitute.org/uploadedFiles/fraser-ca/Content/research-news/research/publications/intermodalsafety-in-the-transport

[104] See, for example: Rory Johnston, "Train vs. Pipeline: What's the Safest Way to Transport Oil?" *Christian Science Monitor*, Energy Voices blog, October 22, 2013,

http://www.csmonitor.com/Environment/Energy-Voices/2013/1022/   Train-vs.-pipeline-What-s-the-safest-way-to-transport-oil.

[105] Platts, *Oilgram Price Report*, January through April 2014.

[106] Phillips 66 Earnings Conference Call, Q2 2013, July 31, 2013.

[107] The Senate Energy and Natural Resources Committee held a hearing on this issue on January 30, 2014. For further information and analysis on oil exports, see CRS Report R43442, *U.S. Crude Oil Export Policy: Background and Considerations*, by Phillip Brown et al.

[108] See, for example, the comments of Sierra Club official Michael Marx in Blake Sobczak, "Environmentalists 'get real creative' to combat oil by rail," *Energy Wire*, January 13, 2014.

In: Waterborne and Rail Transport of U.S. ...   ISBN: 978-1-63463-003-0
Editor: Patrick Williams   © 2014 Nova Science Publishers, Inc.

Chapter 3

CRUDE OIL PROPERTIES RELEVANT TO RAIL TRANSPORT SAFETY: IN BRIEF[*]

Anthony Andrews

SUMMARY

The dramatic increase in U.S. crude oil production, coupled with the increase in crude oil transport by rail, has raised questions about whether properties (e.g., flammability) of these crude types—particularly Bakken crude oil from North Dakota—differ sufficiently from other crude oils to warrant any additional handling considerations. The U.S. Pipeline and Hazardous Materials Safety Administration (PHMSA) issued a Safety Alert to notify emergency responders, shippers, carriers, and the public that recent derailments and resulting fires indicate that the type of crude oil transported from the Bakken region of North Dakota may be more flammable than traditional heavy crude oil. The alert reminds emergency responders that light sweet crude oil, such as that coming from the Bakken region, pose significant fire risk if released from the package (tank car) in an accident. PHMSA has expanded the scope of lab testing to include other factors that affect proper characterization and classification of crude oil such as volatility, corrosivity, hydrogen sulfide content and composition/concentration of the entrained gases in the material.

---

[*] This is an edited, reformatted and augmented version of a Congressional Research Service publication, No. R43401, dated February 18, 2014.

All crude oils are flammable, to a varying degree. Further, crude oils exhibit other potentially hazardous characteristics as well. The growing perception is that light volatile crude oil, like Bakken crude, is a root cause for catastrophic incidents and thus may be too hazardous to ship by rail. However, equally hazardous and flammable liquids from other sources are routinely transported by rail, tanker truck, barge, and pipeline, though not without accident.

A key question for Congress is whether the characteristics of Bakken crude oil make it particularly hazardous to ship by rail, or are there other causes of transport incidents, such as poor maintenance practices, inadequate safety standards, or human error.

INTRODUCTION

The dramatic increase in U.S. and Canadian crude oil production in recent years, coupled with the increase in crude oil transport by rail, has raised questions about whether properties (e.g., flammability) of these crude types— particularly Bakken crude oil from North Dakota and Canada's oil sands— differ sufficiently from other crude oils to warrant any additional handling considerations.[1] The U.S. Pipeline and Hazardous Materials Safety Administration (PHMSA) recently fined several oil companies for improperly classifying their crude oil rail shipments. Potential safety concerns have similarly been raised over pipeline shipments of crude oil from Canada's oil sands projects.[2]

Crude oil is highly variable and can exhibit a wide range of physical and chemical properties. In fact, crude oil samples drawn from the same oil field can vary significantly. Lighter oils may be prone to ignite more readily than heavier crude oils depending on the range of light hydrocarbons they contain. In addition to flammability, other factors such as specific gravity (density) and entrained gases may also play important factors in rail car loading, and corrosivity and sulfur content may affect rail car structural integrity. Bakken crude oil (traded as North Dakota Light) is a light sweet crude oil high in light-end paraffinic range hydrocarbons,[3] as well as heavy-end asphaltic range hydrocarbons.[4] Light sweet crudes, like Bakken, are easier to process directly into gasoline and middle-distillate fuels (e.g., diesel) than heavier crude oils.[5]

PHMSA has issued a Safety Alert to notify emergency responders, shippers, carriers, and the public that recent derailments and resulting fires indicate that the type of crude oil transported from the Bakken region of North Dakota may be more **flammable** than traditional heavy crude oil.[6] Under

PHMSA's "Operation Classification," as it is officially known, tank car inspections will determine whether a tank car's contents are properly classified based on factors that include **volatility, corrosivity, hydrogen sulfide** content and the composition or concentration of **entrained gases** inside the contents.

PHMSA is reinforcing the requirement to properly test, characterize, classify, and, where appropriate, sufficiently degasify hazardous materials prior to and during transportation. "Operation Classification" will be an ongoing effort, and PHMSA will continue to collect samples and measure the characteristics of Bakken crude as well as oil from other locations.

This report discusses the properties that PHMSA addressed in its safety alert, provides background on the composition of various U.S. crude oils, and compares Bakken crude oil to other crude oil produced or transported in the United States.

Flammability

There is some risk with mixing any type of crude oil with air in the proper proportion, in the presence of a source of ignition, which can cause rapid combustion or an explosion.[7] This proportion is the "flammable range" and or alternatively the "explosive range." The flammable range includes all concentrations of flammable vapor or gas in air, in which a flash will occur or a flame will travel if the mixture is ignited at or above a certain temperature (flash point). The Lower Flammable Limit (LFL) is the minimum concentration of vapor or gas in air below which propagation of flame does not occur on contact with a source of ignition. The Upper Flammable Limit (UFL) defines the maximum proportion of vapor in air above which propagation of flame does not occur. The terms Lower Explosive Limit (LEL) and Upper Explosive Limit (UEL) are used interchangeably with LFL and UFL.

Liquids having a flash point at or above 100°F (37.8°C) are classed as "combustible" and below 100°F (37.8°C) as "flammable." Crude oils may differ in terms of combustibility or flammability depending upon their volatile components. The Occupational Safety and Health Administration (OSHA) requires manufacturers and shippers of hazardous materials to provide Material Safety Data Sheets (MSDS) that must include the material's fire and explosive properties, among other properties.[8] PHMSA requires similar reporting information.[9]

According to a Material Safety Data Sheet prepared by Cenovus Energy, Bakken crude has a flash point of 95° F, making it a flammable liquid.[10] Cenovus lists benzene in concentrations of 0.1% to 1% by volume, which is relatively high compared to other crudes. Benzene is a naturally occurring hydrocarbon in the gasoline range and suspected as a cause of Bakken crude's low flash point.

The PHMSA alert reminds emergency responders that light sweet crude oil, such as that coming from the Bakken region, poses significant fire risk if released from the package (tank car) in an incident. Crude oil falls into Department of Transportation (DOT) packing group (PG) I—most serious hazard—or II—moderate hazard.[11] In the recent Lac-Megantic (Quebec) train derailment involving crude shipped from North Dakota, the shippers had reportedly mislabeled the oil as PG III (low hazard).[12]

DOT Package Groups

Packaging Group	Hazard	Flash Point	Boiling Point
I	Most Serious	...	<95° F
II	Moderate	<73° F	>95° F
III	Low	73° −140 °F	>95° F

Note: PG I is determined solely based on boiling point.

In November 2013, the Association of American Railroads (AAR) urged PHMSA to increase federal tank car safety by requiring higher standards for DOT-III tank non-pressure cars built to transport flammable liquids, and all existing cars to be retrofitted to this higher standard or phased out of flammable service.[13] (See "Rail Car Capacity and Load Limit" regarding DOT-III tank cars.) AAR specifically recommended that PHMSA increase design standards for new cars, or require a retrofit of existing cars to eliminate the option for rail shippers to classify a flammable liquid with a flash point between 100 and 140 degrees Fahrenheit as a combustible liquid.

Volatility

Volatility refers to petroleum's evaporation characteristics. ASTM D323-08 *Standard Test Method for Vapor Pressure of Petroleum Products (Reid Method)* is used to determine the vapor pressure at 37.8°C (100°F) of petroleum products and crude oils with initial boiling point above 0°C (32°F).

(ASTM refers to the American Society for Testing and Materials.) Vapor pressure is an important consideration for both crude oil producers and refiners in determining general handling and initial refinery treatment. Vapor pressure also serves as an indirect measure of the evaporation rate of volatile petroleum solvents; with higher vapor pressures indicating greater losses from evaporations. The New York Mercantile Exchange (NYMEX) contract specifications for crude oil futures contracts restrict Reid Vapor Pressure (RVP) to less than 9.5 psi at 100° F.[14] Bakken crude oil has an RVP of at least 8.75.

Corrosivity

Corrosivity due to the presence of naphthenic acids in crude oil is a particular concern for refineries, and had been raised as an issue in permitting the Keystone XL pipeline to transport Canadian oil sand derived crude oil. It is measured as the number of milligrams of potassium hydroxide (mgKOH/g) needed to neutralize the acids in one gram of oil, and reported as Total Acid Number (TAN). As a rule-of-thumb, crude oils with a TAN greater than 0.5 are considered potentially corrosive.[15] Bakken crude oil has a TAN of less than 0.1.

The specifications for DOT-III non-pressure tank cars that haul crude oil require a lining with acid-resistant rubber or other approved rubber compound vulcanized or bonded directly to the metal tank.[16] In general, pipelines transporting hazardous liquids must use inhibitors to mitigate internal corrosion. In the specific case of the proposed Keystone XL pipeline, the potential for corrosion is linked to the basic sediment and water entrained in the crude oil.[17]

Sulfur/Hydrogen Sulfide

A crude oil's free sulfur content is an indication of potential corrosiveness from the formation of acidic sulfur compounds. Sulfur oxides released into the air during combustion of refined petroleum products are also a major air pollutant. During the decomposition of organic matter that occurs with hydrocarbons in some geologic formations, sulfur may chemically combine with hydrogen to form hydrogen sulfide gas (H_2S), a highly corrosive, flammable, and toxic gas. Oil and gas reservoirs with high concentrations of

H_2S can be particularly problematic to produce. H_2S causes sulfide-stress-corrosion cracking in the standard steel casing and valves used to construct oil wells, and thus require a switch to costly stainless steel. PHMSA has a similar concern for sulfide-stress-corrosion in tank cars. During drilling, detection of H_2S could result in abandoning the well due to concerns for worker safety.[18] (Worker exposure to no more than 0.03 ppm for up to 8 hours is generally considered safe.)

Sulfur content is measured as an overall percentage (by weight) of free sulfur and sulfur compounds in a crude oil. Total sulfur content in crude oils generally ranges from below 0.05% to 5%. Crude oils with less than 0.5% free sulfur or other sulfur-containing compounds are typically referred to as "sweet," and above 0.5% sulfur as "sour."[19] Light-sweet crude, however, may contain H_2S. Bakken crude oil is sweet (below 0.25% free sulfur); however, H_2S may occur at problematic levels. In May 2013, Enbridge Energy Partners (a crude oil shipper) detected H_2S at concentrations of 1,200 parts-per-million in a crude oil storage tank.[20] Enbridge consequently made an emergency application to the Federal Energy Regulatory Commission (FERC) to amend its conditions of carriage, which would give it the right to reject crude containing more than 5 parts-per-million H_2S (an exposure level that would require personal protective equipment).[21]

Composition/Concentration of Entrained Gases

The classic image of a "gusher" spraying crude oil up into the air through a drilling derrick is typically the result of dissolved methane (under pressure) that provides a conventional petroleum reservoir with a natural gas drive to move the liquid to the surface. This type of liquid/gas mixture is common—to varying degrees—for crude oil, which contains a range of hydrocarbons, ranging from very light and volatile methane (natural gas) and "condensate" (ethane, propane, butane and pentane) through natural gasoline to complex heavy asphaltenes (asphalt). When crude oil reaches the surface, the reduced pressure and temperature releases the dissolved condensates to a gaseous phase. Surface processing equipment separates the gas into various product streams. The "degassed" oil is typically stored in stock tanks before transport (by pipeline, tank truck, or rail car) to a refinery where any remaining condensate may be separated. The Bakken formation produces both crude oil and natural gas. Due to the lack of pipelines to move the gas to a market, it has been flared (combusted) along with any associated natural gas liquids (analogous to condensate). Bakken crude oil is relatively rich in condensates, compared to similar crude oils.

OTHER CRUDE OIL PROPERTIES

Crude oils differ in density (mass per unit volume), and are typically measured in terms of degrees API Gravity (API refers to the American Petroleum Institute). [22] Higher API gravity corresponds with lighter density. Light crude oils generally exceed 38° API, intermediate crudes fall in the range of 22 to 38° API gravity, and heavy crudes fall below 22° API gravity. Bakken crude ranges from 39.7 to 42.2 ° API gravity.

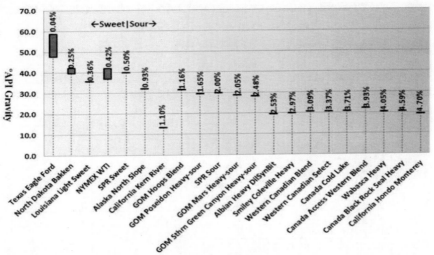

Source: Source: Various, including Capline, http://www.caplinepipeline.com /Reports1.aspx; Canadian Crude Quick Reference Guide Version 0.54, Crude Oil Quality Association, 2009, http://www.coqa- inc.org/102209Canadian CrudeReferenceGuide.pdf; http://www.genesisny.net /Commodity/Oil/OSpecs. html; BP http://www.bp.com/productfamily.do? category Id=16002776 &contentId=7020157; McQuilling Services, LLC, "Carriage of Heavy Grade Oil," Garden City, NY, 2011, http://www.meglobaloil.com/MARPOL.pdf; Hydrocarbon Publishing Co., Opportunity Crudes Report II, Southeastern, PA, 2011, p. 5, http://www.hydrocarbonpublishing.com/ReportP/Prospectus-Opportunity%20 Crudes%20II_2011.pdf.

Figure 1. API Gravity vs. % Sulfur of Crude Oils Produced or Moved Through the United States.

Light sweet crude has less than 0.5% sulfur. Crude oil futures contracts traded on the New York Mercantile Exchange (NYMEX) are based on West Texas Intermediate (WTI), a particular grade of light sweet crude oil. WTI ranges from 37 to 42° API gravity, has sulfur less than 0.42% by weight, and TAN of 0.28 mgKOH/G. Bakken is comparable to WTI in terms of °API gravity and sulfur (see **Table 1**). Its sulfur content is less than 0.25% by weight, making it a sweet crude oil. Its TAN is less than 0.1 mgKOH/g, making it relatively non-corrosive and comparable to WTI.

Figure 1 displays various crude oils produced in the United States by API gravity, and sulfur. Bakken (North Dakota Light Sweet) represents the lighter range of crude oil currently produced in the United States, but by no means the lightest. That title belongs to Texas Eagle Ford crude oil.

Table 1. API Gravity, Sulfur Content, and TAN for Crude Oils Produced or Moved in the United States

Crude Type	°API Gravity	Sulfur Weight %	TAN mgKOH/g
Texas Eagle Ford	47.7 - 58.8	0.04 - 0.1	0.02 - 0.03
Bakken (North Dakota Light/Sweet)	39.7 - 42.2	0.152 - 0.25	<0.1
NYMEX WTI	37.0 - 42.0	<0.42	0.28
Louisiana Light Sweet (LLS)	35.8	0.36	0.5
Alaska North Slope	32.1	0.93	0.12
Strategic Petroleum Reserve sweet/sour	30.0 - 40.0	0.5 - 2.0	0.15 - 0.16
GOM Hoops Blend	31.6	1.16	0.78
GOM Poseidon Heavy-sour	29.7	1.65	0.41
GOM Mars Heavy-sour	28.9	2.05	0.51
GOM Southern Green Canyon Heavy-sour	28.4	2.48	0.17
California Hondo Monterey	19.4	4.70	0.43
California Kern River	13.4	1.10	2.36
Canada Access Western Blend	22.3	3.93	1.72
Canada Cold Lake	20.8	3.71	0.92
Canada Black Rock Seal Heavy	20.7	4.59	1.84
Western Canadian Blend	20.7	3.09	0.66
Western Canadian Select	20.6	3.37	0.87
Wabasca Heavy	20.4	4.05	0.97
Smiley Coleville Heavy	20.0	2.97	0.93
Albian Heavy DilSynBit	19.5	2.53	0.50

Source: Various, including Capline, http://www.caplinepipeline.com/Reports1.aspx; Canadian Crude Quick Reference Guide Version 0.54, Crude Oil Quality Association, 2009, http://www.coqa- inc.org/102209CanadianCrudeReference

Guide.pdf;   http://www.genesisny.net/Commodity/Oil/OSpecs.html;   BP
http://www.bp.com/productfamily.do?categoryId=16002776&contentId=7020157
McQuilling Services, LLC, "Carriage of Heavy Grade Oil," Garden City, NY,
2011, http://www.meglobaloil.com/MARPOL.pdf; Hydrocarbon Publishing Co.,
Opportunity Crudes Report II, Southeastern, PA, 2011, p. 5,
http://www.hydrocarbonpublishing.com/ReportP/Prospectus-Opportunity%20
Crudes%20II_2011.pdf.

As shown in **Table 2**, Bakken's API gravity is slightly higher than WTI,
2% higher in condensates (light end hydrocarbons), but lower than WTI's
upper RVP limit (leaving comparative volatilities open to interpretation).
However, Bakken does fall within the upper and lower range of Eagle Ford
RVP, which is the lightest crude oil produced in the United States.

Table 2. Properties of Representative Crude Oils
Distillate Fractions in percent (percentage)

Crude Oil	API°	RVP	Condensate %
Eagle Ford	47.7 - 58.8	6.5 - 9.3	1.13
Bakken	>41	8.75	3.0
NYMEX WTI	40	<9.5	1.0
LLS	36.2	2.38	2.0

Source: Grace Catalyst Technologies, *Processing shale oils in FCC: Challenges and
Opportunities* (Table 1), Capline Pipeline, Most Current Approve Assay List
http://www.caplinepipeline.com/Reports1.aspx, Platts, *Methodology and
Specification Guide—The Eagle Ford marker: Rational and Methodology.*
Notes: Condensates are light end hydrocarbons in the range C2-C5 and include ethane,
propane, butane, and pentane.

RAIL CAR CAPACITY AND LOAD LIMIT

DOT-111 type tanks cars are "non-pressure" tank cars designed to carry a
wide range of products including hazardous and non-hazardous materials.[23]
Generally, they cannot exceed 34,500 gallons in capacity or 263,000 lbs. in
gross weight on rail.[24] However, the Associate Administrator for Safety,
Federal Railroad Administration (FRA) can approve a non-pressure tank car
loaded up to 286,000 lbs. in gross weight on rail, if it does not contain
"poisonous-by-inhalation" material, and operates under controlled interchange
conditions agreed to by participating railroads.

A tank car becomes overloaded when it exceeds either the maximum gross weight on rail or maximum filling limit. An overloaded rail car can cause its axles to break, or cause the car to exceed the maximum time a car can take to achieve maximum braking.[25] A crude oil shipper has two options in meeting the weight agreement with the rail carrier: provide either a weight from a certified scale, or a weight estimate based on calculations.[26] To calculate the weight limit, the shipper must consider the "light weight" of the tank car (the unloaded or tare weight) and consider the density (API gravity) of the crude oil to be loaded. For illustrative purposes, Figure 2 shows how increasingly heavier API gravity reduces the volume of crude oil that can be loaded into a tank car in order to not exceed the gross rail weight limit.[27]

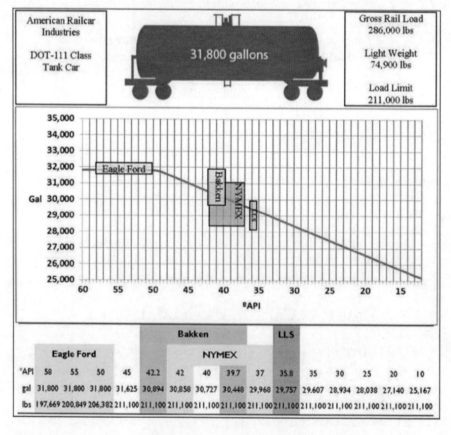

Figure 2. Rail Car Volume vs. °API Gravity; Volumetric Loading Limit.

At 50°API, the tank car can hold its maximum volume of 31,800 gallons and not exceed the 286,000 lb. gross weight on rail limit. At 47.3°API, the shipper must begin reducing volume of crude oil loaded into the tank car. At Bakken's highest density of 39.7°API, the tank car can only hold 30,488 gallons—a volume reduction of roughly 1,300 gallons. The reduced volume also creates free space at the top of the tank car, which provides the opportunity for entrained gases to release from crude oil.

As crude oil density (and thus API gravity) is temperature dependent, volume will increase as temperature increases. Thus, shippers may have to reduce the volume of crude oil loaded in order to accommodate expansion during shipping.

POLICY CONSIDERATIONS

Crude oil shipments by rail have increased in recent years with the development of oil fields in North Dakota. With several derailments and releases of Bakken crude oil, regulators and others are concerned that it contains chemical constituents that exacerbate its volatility and thus its flammability. Absent new pipeline capacity, rail provides the primary "takeaway" capacity for Bakken producers. Unit train shipments of Bakken crude now supply refineries on both the East and West Coasts. However, the U.S. Gulf Coast (Texas and Louisiana) constitutes the most prolific region of domestic crude oil production, and the crude oils produced (WTI, Eagle Ford, and Louisiana Light Sweet, among others) rival Bakken in the characteristics the PHMSA alert has called into scrutiny. The Gulf Coast does benefit from existing pipeline infrastructure; however, producers are relying on rail to access new markets, as evidenced by Eagle Ford crude oil moving from East Texas to St James, Louisiana by rail.[28]

All crude oils are flammable, to a varying degree. Further, crude oils exhibit other potentially hazardous characteristics as well. The growing perception is that light volatile crude oil, like Bakken crude, is a root cause for catastrophic incidents and thus may be too hazardous to ship by rail. However, equally hazardous and flammable liquids from other sources are routinely transported by rail, tanker truck, barge, and pipeline, though not without incident.

A key question for Congress is whether the characteristics of Bakken crude oil make it particularly hazardous. Conversely, does focusing so much attention on the commodity distract from other causes of transport incidents, such as maintenance practices, safety standards and human error? A further policy question is whether Bakken crude oil significantly differs from other crude oils that the standard practices do not apply, and if so, what policy steps should be taken to remedy safety concerns?

End Notes

[1] See CRS Report R42032, The Bakken Formation: Leading Unconventional Oil Development, by Michael Ratner et al., and CRS Report RL34258, North American Oil Sands: History of Development, Prospects for the Future, by Marc Humphries.

[2] See CRS Report R42611, Oil Sands and the Keystone XL Pipeline: Background and Selected Environmental Issues, coordinated by Jonathan L. Ramseur.

[3] Paraffins are simple chain hydrocarbons.

[4] K.J. Bryden, E.T. Habib Jr., and O.A. Topete, "Processing Shale Oils in FCC: Challenges and Opportunities," Hydrocarbon Processing, September 1, 2013, http://www.hydrocarbon processing.com/Article/3250397/Processingshale-oils-in-FCC-Challenges-and-opportunities

[5] See CRS Report R41478, The U.S. Oil Refining Industry: Background in Changing Markets and Fuel Policies, by Anthony Andrews et al.

[6] The Pipeline and Hazardous Materials Safety Administration, "Safety Alert—January 2, 2014, Preliminary Guidance from OPERATION CLASSIFICATION." This advisory is a follow-up to the PHMSA and Federal Railroad Administration (FRA) joint safety advisory published November 20, 2013 [78 FR 69745], http://www.phmsa.dot.gov.

[7] Department of Labor, Occupational Safety and Health Administration, Flammable and Combustible Liquids—29 C.F.R. 1910.106, https://www.osha.gov/dte/library /flammable_liquids

[8] Material Safety Data Sheets may be used to comply with OSHA's Hazard Communication Standard, 29 CFR 1910.1200. Standard must be consulted for specific requirements.

[9] 49 C.F.R. Parts 172 and 173.

[10] Cenovus Energy Inc., 500 Centre Street Se, PO Box 766, Calgary, AB T2P OM5.

[11] 49 C.F.R. Part 173, Subpart D—Definitions Classification, Packing Group Assignments and Other Exceptions for Hazardous Materials Other Than Class 1 and Class 7.

[12] Monique Beaudin, "Crude Oil in Lac-Megantic Derailment Was Mislabeled, Transportation Safety Board Says," The Gazette, October 7, 2013, http://www.montrealgazette.com/ Crude+M%C3%A9gantic+derailment+mislabelled+Transportation+Safety+Board+says/88 98364/story.html.

[13] Association of American Railroads, Railroad Tank Cars, https://www.aar.org/safety /Documents/Railroad%20Tank%20Cars.pdf.

[14] CME Group, NYMEX Rulebook, Chapter 200 – Light Sweet Crude Oil Futures. CME references RVP of less than 9.5 pounds per square inch at 100 degrees Fahrenheit by ASTM-5191-96 Standard Test Method for Vapor Pressure of Petroleum Products (Mini Method).

[15] R.D. Kane and M.S. Cayard, "A Comprehensive Study of Naphthenic Acid Corrosion," Paper No. 02555, Corrosion 2002, http://www.icorr.net/wp-content/uploads/2011/01/napthenic_ corrosion.pdf.

[16] 49 C.F.R. 179 Subpart D—Specification for Non-Pressure Tank Cars (Classes DOT−111AW and 115AW).

[17] Per 49 C.F.R. 195.579: "Keystone must limit basic sediment and water (BS&W) to 0.5 percent by volume and report BS&W testing results to PHMSA in the annual report. Keystone must also report upset conditions causing BS&W level excursions above the limit." From Final Supplemental Environmental Impact Statement, Keystone XL Project Appendix B Potential Releases and Pipeline Safety Condition 34 Internal Corrosion, U.S. Department of State, http://keystonepipeline-xl.state

[18] Paradoxically, H2S is potentially lethal but odorless at high concentrations while at low concentrations H2S has an offensive odor similar to rotten eggs. Exposure to 10 ppm for more than 10 minutes causes eye and throat injuries, 500 ppm for 3 to 5 minutes results in unconsciousness. Alken Murray Corp, Toxicity to Hydrogen Sulfide Gas, http://www.alken-murray.com/H2SREM9.HTM.

[19] 10 JDL Oil and Gas Exploration, Inc., "Crude Oil Basics," web page, July 28, 2011, http://www.jdloil.com/ oil_basics.htm.

[20] John Kemp, "Toxic Gas in Bakken Pipeline Points to Sour Well Problem: Kemp," Reuters, May 29, 2013, http://www.reuters.com/article/2013/05/29/column-kemp-bakken-pipelines-idUSL5N0EA3SU20130529.

[21] FERC Docket IS13-273-000).

[22] API gravity is measured with a Baume hydrometer gradated in degrees so that most values fall between 10° and 70° API gravity A Baume hydrometer is also used in auto repair shops for testing radiator fluid.

[23] 949 C.F.R. Part 179, Subpart D—Specifications for Non-Pressure Tank Car Tanks (Classes DOT-111AW and 115AW).

[24] 49 C.F.R. 179.13, Tank Car Capacity and Gross Weight Limitation.

[25] The Federal Railroad Administration, under C.F.R. Part 49, specifies the maximum time each car can take to achieve maximum braking. From "An Introduction to Train Brakes," by John Bentley, http://www.tarorigin.com/art/Jbentley/.

[26] ICC Uniform Freight Classification 6000-J, Rule 35.

[27] For further information, refer to Federal Railroad Administration, Tank Car Filling Limit & Filling Density Standards, http://www.fra.dot.gov/eLib/details/L04699.

[28] Gabe Ortt, EOG Resources: Moving ahead with railroad demand and cost cutting, Seeking Alpha, December 30, 2013, http://seekingalpha.com/article/1920411-eog-resources

In: Waterborne and Rail Transport of U.S. ...   ISBN: 978-1-63463-003-0
Editor: Patrick Williams   © 2014 Nova Science Publishers, Inc.

Chapter 4

OIL SPILLS IN U.S. COASTAL WATERS: BACKGROUND AND GOVERNANCE*

Jonathan L. Ramseur

SUMMARY

The impacts of an oil spill depend on the size of the spill, the rate of the spill, the type of oil spilled, and the location of the spill. Depending on timing and location, even a relatively minor spill can cause significant harm to individual organisms and entire populations. Oil spills can cause impacts over a range of time scales, from days to years, or even decades for certain spills.

Based on data between 1973 and 2009, the annual number and volume of oil spills have shown declines—in some cases, dramatic declines. However, this trend was altered dramatically by the 2010 *Deepwater Horizon* oil spill in the Gulf of Mexico. The incident led to a significant release of oil: according to the federal government's estimate, the well released approximately 206 million gallons of oil before it was contained on July 15. The 2010 Gulf oil spill generated considerable interest in oil spill governance issues.

---

* This is an edited, reformatted and augmented version of the Congressional Research Service Publication, CRS Report for Congress RL33705, dated January 14, 2013.

This report provides background information regarding oil spills in U.S. coastal waters and identifies the legal authorities governing oil spill prevention, response, and cleanup. The governing framework for oil spills in the United States remains a combination of federal, state, and international authorities. Within this framework, several federal agencies have the authority to implement oil spill regulations. Agency responsibilities can be divided into two categories: (1) oil spill response and cleanup and (2) oil spill prevention/preparedness.

Oil spill response authority is determined by the location of the spill: the U.S. Coast Guard has response authority in the U.S. coastal zone, and the Environmental Protection Agency covers the inland zone. Jurisdiction over oil spill prevention and preparedness duties is determined by the potential sources (e.g., vessels, facilities, pipelines) of oil spills.

As with the *Exxon Valdez* oil spill in 1989, the 2010 *Deepwater Horizon* spill generated significant attention to various oil spill policy matters, including prevention, preparedness, response, and liability and compensation. The 111th Congress enacted three oil spill-related proposals into law (P.L. 111-191, P.L. 111-212, and P.L. 111-281), but these laws generally concerned short-term matters that will not have a lasting impact on oil spill governance.

In general, oil spill-related issues garnered less attention during the 112th Congress. The 112th Congress enacted two statutes that contain oil spill-related provisions. P.L. 112-90 includes several oil spill-related provisions involving pipelines. P.L. 112-141 includes a subtitle referred to as the RESTORE Act. This act directs 80% of any administrative and civil Clean Water Act Section 311 penalties connected with the 2010 *Deepwater Horizon* oil spill into a newly created trust fund. Monies from this fund, through various mechanisms, will support environmental and economic restoration in the Gulf states.

INTRODUCTION

Oil is a dominant source of energy in the United States, supplying the nation with approximately 36% of its energy needs.[1] Its use is widespread, providing fuel for the transportation, industrial, and residential sectors. Vast quantities of oil continuously enter the country via vessel or pipeline and are then transported to destinations throughout the country. With such widespread use and nonstop movement, it is inevitable that some number of spills will occur.

Over the past few decades, several major U.S. oil spills have had lasting repercussions that transcended the local environmental and economic effects. The April 2010 oil spill in the Gulf of Mexico (see text box) has intensified interest in many oil spill-related issues. Prior to the 2010 Gulf spill, the most notable example was the 1989 *Exxon Valdez* spill, which released approximately 11 million gallons (260,000 barrels) of crude oil into Prince William Sound, Alaska. The *Exxon Valdez* spill[2] produced extensive consequences beyond Alaska. According to the National Academies of Science, the *Exxon Valdez* disaster caused "fundamental changes in the way the U.S. public thought about oil, the oil industry, and the transport of petroleum products by tankers ... 'big oil' was suddenly seen as a necessary evil, something to be feared and mistrusted."[3]

DEEPWATER HORIZON OIL SPILL IN THE GULF OF MEXICO

On April 20, 2010, an explosion occurred at the *Deepwater Horizon* drilling platform in the Gulf of Mexico, resulting in 11 fatalities. The incident disabled the facility and led to a full evacuation before the platform sank into the Gulf on April 22. A significant release of oil at the sea floor was soon discovered. According to the National Incident Command's Flow Rate Technical Group estimate of August 2, 2010, the well released approximately 206 million gallons of oil (4.9 million barrels) before it was contained.

The following websites provide additional information:

- Federal government's website for the oil spill response and recovery, at http://www.restorethegulf.gov/
- EPA website, at http://www.epa.gov/bpspill/
- NOAA website, at http://www.noaa.gov/deepwaterhorizon/

This report provides background information regarding oil spills[4] in U.S. coastal waters[5] and identifies the legal authorities governing oil spill prevention, response, and cleanup.[6] The first section highlights background issues, including oil spill statistics and potential environmental impacts. The second section discusses the legal and regulatory framework that governs oil spill prevention and response.

BACKGROUND

Oil Inputs

Oil enters coastal waters of the United States from a wide variety of sources. These sources vary considerably. Some sources, such as discharges from recreational vessels, emit relatively minor amounts per individual release but have numerous annual releases, which, in aggregate, contribute a significant annual volume. Other sources, such as spills from oil tankers, release oil on a less frequent basis but have the potential to release a significant volume in one incident. These variances in frequency and volume of oil releases create different environmental impacts as well as different challenges for responders and policymakers.

All Sources

A 2003 National Research Council report groups oil releases into four categories: natural seeps, oil consumption, oil transportation, and oil extraction/production.[7] As illustrated in **Figure 1**, the majority of oil in U.S. waters comes from natural seeps—geologic openings on the ocean floor. Well-known natural seeps are found in the Gulf of Mexico and off the coast of southern California, regions with extensive oil exploration and production. Although the seeps release large volumes of oil each year,[8] the surrounding ecosystem can adapt, and even thrive, because the rate of release is relatively slow.[9]

The vast majority of oil introduced to the environment through human behavior falls into the consumption category. This category is broad in scope and includes land-based sources,[10] operational discharges from commercial vessels[11] and recreational craft,[12] and atmospheric deposition of petroleum hydrocarbons.[13] The quantitative value and the environmental fate of many of these sources are poorly understood. For example, oil from land-based sources—the largest estimated component of the consumption category—may not directly enter U.S. coastal waters until traveling through various man-made conveyances, such as storm-water drains. As such, the range of uncertainty of land-based runoff is substantial, from a minimum annual estimate of 5.6 million gallons to 588 million gallons.[14]

Potential Sources of Major Spills

Although oil transportation and oil extraction activities contribute (on average) a relatively small percentage of oil to U.S. waters (see **Figure 1**), sources within these sectors have generated major oil spills in U.S. coastal waters. Oil spill policy in the United States has generally focused on prevention, preparation, and response involving oil spills from these (and several other) sources.

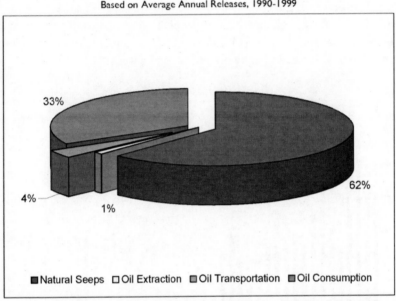

Figure 1. Estimates of Percentage Contribution of Oil into North American Coastal Waters, by Major Source Categories.

Source: Prepared by the Congressional Research Service (CRS) with data from the National Research Council (NRC) of the National Academies of Science, 2003, *Oil in the Sea III: Inputs, Fates, and Effects*, p. 69.

Notes: Extraction includes platform spills, produced waters, and atmospheric deposition. Transportation includes spills from tanker/barges, pipelines, coastal facilities, and atmospheric deposition. Oil consumption includes river and urban runoff, oil spills from cargo ships, operational discharges from commercial vessels and recreational craft, and atmospheric deposition. For further details of these inputs, see the NRC Report.

Figure 2 illustrates the combined number and volume of oil spills from selected sources, whose spills would likely impact U.S. coastal waters. These sources include oil tankers and barges, facilities, and pipelines, among others.[15] Prior to the 2010 Gulf spill, data between 1973 and 2009 indicate that both the number of spills and volume of oil entering U.S. coastal waters have declined; in some years, the declines have been dramatic.[16] Including the 2010 *Deepwater Horizon* oil spill (approximately 200 million gallons) would dramatically alter the volume trendline.

Figure 3 compares the volume of spills over time from the same selected sources identified in **Figure 2**. As **Figure 3** illustrates, the primary source of oil spills in coastal waters has been oil tankers and barges. The substantial drop in the annual *spill volume* (illustrated in both figures) is most attributable to the decline in volume spilled by oil tankers and barges.

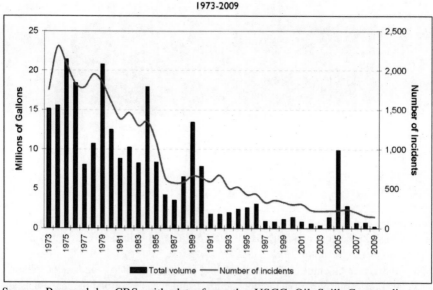

Source: Prepared by CRS with data from the USCG Oil Spill Compendium, at https://homeport.uscg.mil (click on "Investigations"). Accessed in January 2013.
Notes: The Coast Guard states that its Oil Spill Compendium includes spills that have been "investigated" by the Coast Guard. Further, "this data is provided 'as reported,' with no interpretation or filtering. For example, incidents that fall within the jurisdiction of other agencies, or that are not required to be reported under existing Coast Guard regulations, may be included in the compendium."

Figure 2. Annual Volume and Number of Oil Spills from Selected Sources.

1973-2009

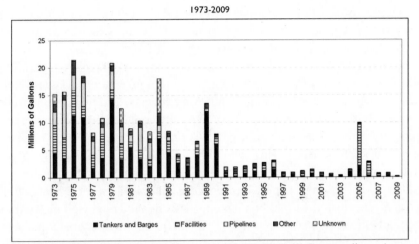

Source: Prepared by CRS with data from the USCG Oil Spill Compendium. Accessed in January 2013.

Notes: The Coast Guard states that its Oil Spill Compendium includes spills that have been "investigated" by the Coast Guard. Further, "this data is provided 'as reported,' with no interpretation or filtering. For example, incidents that fall within the jurisdiction of other agencies, or that are not required to be reported under existing Coast Guard regulations, may be included in the compendium." Other sources include non-tanker vessels, such as cargo ships, passenger vessels, fishing vessels, and recreational vessels. For a complete list see the USCG Oil Spill Compendium at https://homeport.uscg.mil (click on "Investigations").

Figure 3. Comparison of Estimated Oil Spill Volumes from Selected Sources.

The volume of oil spilled from vessels in U.S. waters in the 1990s differed dramatically from the volume spilled in the previous decades. This historical decline of *spill incidents* is likely related, at least in part, to international oil pollution standards that went into effect in 1983. These new standards were implemented in the United States by the Act to Prevent Pollution from Ships (discussed later in this report).[17]

In addition, the *Exxon Valdez* spill of 1989 and the resulting Oil Pollution Act of 1990 (OPA) played key roles in the subsequent spill volume reduction. The 1990 Act (discussed below) made comprehensive changes to U.S. oil pollution law by expanding federal response authority and increasing spill liability. The high costs associated with the *Exxon Valdez* spill,[18] and the threat of broad liability imposed by OPA (in some scenarios, unlimited liability), have likely been the central drivers for the spill volume decline seen in the 1990s. In addition to international and federal governance, 28 states had oil spill liability laws, 19 of which imposed unlimited liability, before the *Exxon Valdez* spill occurred in 1989.[19] After the 1989 spill, some states enacted additional legislation,[20] which may have contributed to the declines.

Although the volume of oil spills from oil tankers and barges has dwarfed other selected sources, the 2010 Gulf spill highlighted the worst-case discharge potential of spills from offshore oil extraction activities. Spills from offshore platforms and pipelines have typically represented (on an annual basis) only a relatively minor (only 0.05%) component of the total input to North American waters.[21] However, oil well blowouts from offshore oil extraction operations have historically been a source of major oil spills. Before the 2010 Gulf spill, the largest unintentional oil spill in world history—the *IXTOC I*, estimated at 140 million gallons—was due to an oil well blowout in Mexican Gulf Coast waters in 1979.[22] The 2010 *Deepwater Horizon* incident released approximately 206 million gallons of oil (4.9 million barrels) before it was contained.[23] As a comparison, the largest oil tanker spill in world history—the *Atlantic Empress* off the coast of Tobago in 1979—was estimated at approximately 84 million gallons.[24]

Impacts of Oil Spills in Aquatic Environments

The impacts of an oil spill depend on the size of the spill, the rate of the spill, the type of oil spilled, and the location of the spill. Depending on timing and location, even a relatively minor spill can cause significant harm to individual organisms and entire populations.[25] Oil spills can cause impacts over a range of time scales, from days to years, or even decades for certain spills. Impacts are typically divided into acute (short-term) and chronic (long-term) effects. Both types are part of a complicated and often controversial equation that is addressed after an oil spill: ecosystem recovery.

Acute Impacts

Depending on the toxicity and concentration of the spill, acute exposure to oil spills can kill various organisms and cause the following debilitating (but not necessarily lethal) effects:[26]

- reduced reproduction,
- altered development,
- impaired feeding mechanisms, and
- decreased defense from disease.

Birds, marine mammals, bottom-dwelling and intertidal species, and organisms in their developmental stages (e.g., fish eggs and larvae) are particularly vulnerable to oil spills.[27]

In addition to the impacts to individual organisms, oil spills can lead to a disruption of the structure and function of the ecosystem. Certain habitats—such as coral reefs, mangrove swamps, and salt marshes—are especially vulnerable, because the physical structure of the habitats depends upon living organisms.

These potential acute effects to individual organisms and marine ecosystems have been "unambiguously established" by laboratory studies and well-studied spills.[28]

Chronic Impacts

Long-term, chronic exposure typically occurs from continuous oil releases—leaking pipelines, offshore production discharges, and non-point sources (e.g., urban runoff). Although spills are normally associated with acute impacts, some oil spills have also demonstrated chronic exposure and effects.[29] There is increasing evidence that chronic, low-level exposures to oil contaminants can significantly affect the survival and reproductive success of marine birds and mammals.[30] However, because of the complexity of factors, including a longer time period and presence of other pollutants, determining the precise effects on species and ecosystems due to chronic oil exposure in a particular locale is difficult for scientists. As a result, studies involving chronic effects are often met with debate and some controversy.

Ecosystem Recovery

Interested parties may have differing opinions as to what constitutes ecosystem recovery. At one end of the spectrum, local groups may demand that an ecosystem be returned to pre-spill conditions. NOAA regulations (15 C.F.R. §990.30) state that recovery "means the return of injured natural resources and services to baseline"—in other words, a return to conditions as they would have been had the spill not occurred. Baseline conditions may not equate with pre-spill conditions. Multiple variables affect local species and ecosystem services. For example, one species at a spill site could have been on the decline at the time of an incident, because of changing water temperatures. These types of trends are considered during the restoration evaluative process (discussed below). Restoration leaves room for site-specific interpretation, which, in the case of the *Exxon Valdez* spill and cleanup, continues to generate considerable argument.

Economic Costs of Oil Spills

The economic costs that can result from an oil spill can be broken into three categories: cleanup expenses, natural resource damages, and the various economic losses incurred by the affected community or individuals.

Cleanup Costs

The cleanup costs of an oil spill can vary greatly and are influenced by a mix of factors: location characteristics, oil type, and oil volume.

Location

Location is generally considered the most important factor because it involves multiple variables. Areas with less water movement, such as marshlands, will generally cost more to clean up than open water. Some spill locations may have relatively robust populations of indigenous micro-organisms that help degrade the oil naturally.[31]

Tourist destinations or sensitive habitats, such as coral reefs, will likely require more stringent cleanup standards, thus increasing the costs. The political and social culture at the spill site plays a part as well. A spill in a high-profile area may receive special attention.[32] Major oil spills, especially ones that affect shoreline ecosystems, are often met with extensive media coverage, placing pressure on parties to take action. Coupled with this pressure, authorities (federal, state, or local) at these locations may require extensive oil spill response requirements, which can influence cleanup cost. For instance, spill costs in the United States are considerably higher than in other parts of the world.[33]

Oil Type

The more persistent and viscous oil types, such as heavy crude oil and intermediates known as bunker fuels, are more expensive to clean up. Gasoline and other lighter refined products may require only minimal cleanup action. Generally, these materials will evaporate or disperse relatively quickly, leaving only a small volume of petroleum product in the environment.

Oil Volume

Compared with other factors, spill volume is less important. A major spill away from shore will likely cost considerably less than a minor spill in a sensitive location. Certainly, the amount of oil spilled affects cleanup costs, because, all things being equal, a larger spill will require a larger and more expensive cleanup effort. However, the relationship between cleanup costs and spill volume is not linear. Cleaning up a smaller spill is likely to cost more than a larger spill on a per-gallon basis.[34]

Natural Resources Damages

This category of costs relates to the environmental impacts caused by an oil spill. Pursuant to OPA, the party responsible for an oil spill is liable for any loss of natural resources (e.g., fish, animals, plants, and their habitats) and the services provided by the resource (e.g., drinking water, recreation).

When a spill occurs, natural resource trustees conduct a natural resource damage assessment to determine the extent of the harm. Trustees may include officials from federal agencies designated by the President, state agencies designated by the relevant governor, and representatives from tribal and foreign governments.[35] The various trustees assess damages to natural resources under their respective jurisdictions.[36] If multiple trustees are involved, they must select a lead administrative trustee (LAT), who coordinates trustee activities and serves as a liaison between oil spill responders. The LAT need not be from a federal agency; however, only a federal LAT can submit a request to the Oil Spill Liability Trust Fund for the initial assessment funding.[37]

The Oil Pollution Act (OPA) of 1990 states that the measure of natural resource damages includes

- the cost of restoring, rehabilitating, replacing, or acquiring the equivalent of the damaged natural resources;
- the diminution in value of those natural resources pending restoration; and
- the reasonable cost of assessing those damages.[38]

Pursuant to OPA, NOAA developed regulations pertaining to natural resource damage assessments in 1996.[39] Natural resource damages may include both losses of direct use and passive uses. Direct use value may derive from recreational (e.g., boating), commercial (e.g., fishing), or cultural or historical uses of the resource. In contrast, a passive-use value may derive from preserving the resource for its own sake or for enjoyment by future generations.[40]

The damages are compensatory, not punitive. Collected damages cannot be placed into the general Treasury revenues of the federal or state government, but must be used to restore or replace lost resources.[41] Indeed, NOAA's regulations focus on the costs of primary restoration— returning the resource to its baseline condition—and compensatory restoration—addressing interim losses of resources and their services.[42]

Other Economic Costs

Oil spills can generate costs other than response expenses or damages to natural resources. An oil spill can disrupt business activity near the spill, particularly businesses and individuals that count on the resources and reputation of the local environment. For example, the local fishing and tourist industry may be affected. In some cases, a well-publicized oil spill can weaken local or regional industries near the spill site, regardless of the actual threat to human health created by the spill.

Local infrastructure and services can be disrupted by an oil spill. Port and harbor operations may be interrupted, altering the flow of trade goods. Power plants that use cooling water systems may need to temporarily cease operations. For example, the Salem Nuclear Plant—the second-largest nuclear plant in the United States—was forced to halt activity due to a substantial oil spill (more than 250,000 gallons) in the Delaware River in November 2004.

OIL SPILL GOVERNANCE

When the *Exxon Valdez* ran aground in March 1989, there were multiple federal statutes, state statutes, and international conventions that dealt with oil discharges. The spill highlighted the inadequacies of the existing coverage and generated public outrage.[43] Following the spill, Members of Congress faced great pressure to address these issues. (See the **Appendix** for further information concerning these issues.) The end result was the Oil Pollution Act of 1990 (OPA)[44]— the first comprehensive law to specifically address oil pollution to waterways and coastlines of the United States.

The governing framework for oil spills in the United States remains a combination of federal, state, and international authorities. Within this framework, several federal agencies have the authority to implement oil spill regulations. The framework and primary federal funding process used to respond to oil spills are described below.

Oil Pollution Act of 1990

With the enactment of OPA on August 18, 1990, Congress consolidated the existing federal oil spill laws under one program (**Appendix**). The 1990 law expanded the existing liability provisions within the Clean Water Act (CWA)[45] and created new free-standing requirements regarding oil spill prevention and response. Key OPA provisions are discussed below.

Spill Response Authority

When responding to a spill, many considered the lines of responsibility under the pre-OPA regime to be unclear,[46] with too much reliance on spillers to perform proper cleanup.[47] OPA strengthened and clarified the federal government's role in oil spill response and cleanup. OPA Section 4201 amended Section 311(c) of the CWA to provide the President (delegated to the U.S. Coast Guard or EPA) with authority to perform cleanup immediately using federal resources,[48] monitor the response efforts of the spiller, or direct the spiller's cleanup activities. The revised response authorities addressed concerns "that precious time would be lost while waiting for the spiller to marshall its cleanup forces."[49]

The federal government—specifically the On-Scene Coordinator (OSC) for spills in the Coast Guard's jurisdiction—determines the level of cleanup required. Although the federal government must consult with designated trustees of natural resources and the governor of the state affected by the spill, the decision that cleanup is completed and can be ended rests with the federal government. States may require further work, but without the support of federal funding.[50]

National Contingency Plan

The first National Oil and Hazardous Substances Pollution Contingency Plan (NCP) was administratively prepared in 1968 after observing the British government's response to a 37- million-gallon oil tanker spill (*Torrey Canyon*) off the coast of England.[51] The NCP contains the federal government's procedures for responding to oil spills and hazardous substance releases.[52]

OPA expanded the role and breadth of the NCP. The 1990 law established a multi-layered planning and response system to improve preparedness and response to spills in marine environments.[53] Among other things, the act also required the President to establish procedures and standards (as part of the NCP) for responding to worst-case oil spill scenarios.[54]

Tank Vessel and Facility Response Plans

As a component of the enhanced NCP, OPA amended the CWA to require that U.S. tank vessels, offshore facilities, and certain onshore facilities[55] prepare and submit oil spill response plans to the relevant federal agency. In general, vessels and facilities are prohibited from handling, storing, or transporting oil if they do not have a plan approved by (or submitted to) the appropriate agency (discussed below).[56]

The plans should, among other things, identify how the owner or operator of a vessel or facility would respond to a worst-case scenario spill. Congress did not intend for every vessel to have onboard all the personnel and equipment needed to respond to a worst-case spill, but vessels must have a plan and procedures to call upon—typically through a contractual relationship—the necessary equipment and personnel for responding to a worst-case spill.[57]

In 2004, Congress enacted an amendment requiring non-tank vessels (i.e., ships carrying oil for their own fuel use) over 400 gross tons to prepare and submit a vessel response plan.[58] Congress reasoned that many non-tank vessels have as much oil onboard as small tank vessels, thus presenting a comparable risk from an oil spill. Moreover, the international standards for oil spill prevention[59] apply to tanker and non-tanker vessels alike. Thus, the 2004 amendment brought the U.S. law more in line with international provisions.

Double-Hull Design for Vessels

The issue of double hulls received considerable debate for many years prior to OPA, and it was one of the stumbling blocks for unified oil spill legislation. Proponents maintained that double- hull construction provides extra protection if a vessel becomes damaged.[60] However, opponents argued that a double-hulled vessel might cause stability problems if an accident occurred, thus negating the benefits.[61] Stakeholders also highlighted the impacts that a double-hull requirement would entail for the shipping industry (e.g., cost and time of retrofitting, ship availability).[62] The OPA requirements for double hulls reflected some of these concerns.

The act required new vessels carrying oil and operating in U.S. waters to have double hulls.[63] However, OPA provided certain exceptions, depending on the size of the vessel (e.g., less than 5,000 gross tons)[64] and its particular use (e.g., lightering).[65] For older vessels, OPA established a staggered retrofitting schedule, based on vessel age and size. As of January 2010, single-hull vessels (with several exceptions, some of which expire in 2015) cannot operate in U.S. waters.

Liability Issues[66]

OPA unified the liability provisions of existing oil spill statutes, creating a freestanding liability regime. Section 1002 states that responsible parties are liable for any discharge of oil (or threat of discharge) from a vessel or facility[67] to navigable waters, adjoining shorelines, or the exclusive economic zone[68] of the United States (i.e., 200 nautical miles beyond the shore).

Regarding the oil spill statutes prior to OPA, Congress recognized that "there is no comprehensive legislation in place that promptly and adequately compensates those who suffer other types of economic loss as a result of an oil pollution incident."[69] OPA broadened the scope of damages (i.e., costs) for which an oil spiller would be liable. Under OPA, a responsible party is liable for all cleanup costs incurred, not only by a government entity, but also by a private party.[70] In addition to cleanup costs, OPA significantly increased the range of liable damages to include the following:

- injury to natural resources,
- loss of personal property (and resultant economic losses),
- loss of subsistence use of natural resources,
- lost revenues resulting from destruction of property or natural resource injury,
- lost profits and earning capacity resulting from property injury or natural resource injury, and
- costs of providing extra public services during or after spill response.[71]

OPA provided limited defenses from liability: act of God, act of war, and act or omission of certain third parties. These defenses are similar to those of the Superfund statute,[72] established in 1980 for releases of hazardous substances (which does not include oil).

Except for certain behavior, including acts of gross negligence or willful misconduct,[73] OPA set liability limits (or caps) for cleanup costs and other damages. Until 2006, liability limits for vessels were based on vessel carrying capacity, generally $1,200 per gross ton. As an example, the liability limit for the 2004 *Athos* tanker spill in Delaware River was approximately $45 million.[74]

OPA requires the President to issue regulations to adjust the liability limits at least every three years to take into account changes in the consumer price index (CPI). Despite this requirement, adjustments to liability limits were not made until Congress amended OPA in July 2006. The Coast Guard and

Maritime Transportation Act of 2006 (P.L. 109-241) increased limits to $1,900/gross ton for double-hulled vessels and $3,000/gross ton for single-hulled vessels. Furthermore, the Coast Guard made its first CPI adjustment to the liability limits in 2009, increasing the limits to $2,000 and $3,200, respectively.[75]

Mobile offshore drilling units (MODUs), like the *Deepwater Horizon* unit involved in the April 2010 incident in the Gulf of Mexico, are first treated as tank vessels for their liability cap. If removal and damage costs exceed this liability cap, a MODU is deemed to be an offshore facility for the excess amount.[76]

Offshore facility liability is unlimited for removal costs but capped at $75 million for other costs and damages; onshore facility and deepwater port liability is limited to $350 million. In contrast to tank vessel liability limits, these liability limits are at the same level as they were in 1990.

The Oil Spill Liability Trust Fund

Prior to OPA, federal funding for oil spill response was generally considered inadequate,[77] and damages recovery was difficult for private parties.[78] To help address these issues, Congress supplemented OPA's expanded range of covered damages with the Oil Spill Liability Trust Fund (OSLTF).

Pursuant to Executive Order (EO) 12777, the Coast Guard created the National Pollution Funds Center (NPFC) to manage the trust fund in 1991. The fund may be used for several purposes:

- prompt payment of costs for responding to and removing oil spills;
- payment of the costs incurred by the federal and state trustees of natural resources for assessing the injuries to natural resources caused by an oil spill, and developing and implementing the plans to restore or replace the injured natural resources;
- payment of parties' claims for uncompensated removal costs, and for uncompensated damages (e.g., financial losses of fishermen, hotels, and beachfront businesses);
- payment for the net loss of government revenue, and for increased public services by a state or its political subdivisions; and
- payment of federal administrative and operational costs, including research and development, and $25 million per year for the Coast Guard's operating expenses.

Although Congress created the OSLTF in 1986,[79] Congress did not authorize its use or provide its funding until after the *Exxon Valdez* incident. In 1990, OPA provided the statutory authorization necessary to put the fund in motion. Through OPA, Congress transferred balances from other federal liability funds[80] into the OSLTF. In complementary legislation, Congress imposed a 5- cent-per-barrel tax on the oil industry to support the fund.[81] Collection of this fee ceased on December 31, 1994, due to a sunset provision in the law. However, in April 2006, the tax resumed as required by the Energy Policy Act of 2005 (P.L. 109-58). In addition, the Emergency Economic Stabilization Act of 2008 (P.L. 110-343) increased the tax rate to 8 cents through 2016. In 2017, the rate increases to 9 cents. The tax is scheduled to terminate at the end of 2017.[82]

Financial Responsibility

To preserve the trust fund and ensure that responsible parties can be held accountable for oil spill cleanup and damages, OPA requires that vessels and offshore facilities maintain evidence of financial responsibility (e.g., insurance). The Coast Guard's National Pollution Funds Center (NPFC) implements the financial responsibility provisions for vessels; the Bureau of Ocean Energy Management, Regulation, and Enforcement (formerly the Minerals Management Service, MMS) implements this requirement for offshore facilities.

The current levels of financial responsibility are related to the current liability limits for various sources (e.g., vessels, offshore facilities) of potential oil spills. The liability limits differ by potential source. In the case of vessels, whose liability limits are a single dollar amount encompassing both removal costs and other damages, the financial responsibility levels are directly tied to the corresponding liability caps. Current law requires responsible parties for vessels to demonstrate the "maximum amount of liability to which the responsible party could be subjected under [the liability limits in OPA Section 1004; 33 U.S.C. 2704]."

Because the structure of offshore facility liability limit is different than vessels, the corresponding financial responsibility limit provisions differ. Responsible parties for offshore facilities in federal waters must demonstrate $35 million financial responsibility, unless the President determines a greater amount (not to exceed $150 million) is justified (33 U.S.C. 2716(c)). The federal regulations that are authored by this statutory provision (30 C.F.R. Part 254) base the financial responsibility amount—between $35 million and $150 million—on a facility's worst-case discharge volume (as defined in 30 C.F.R. §253.14). For example, a facility with a worst-case discharge volume over 105,000 barrels[83]—the highest level of worst-case discharge listed in the regulations—must maintain $150 million in financial responsibility.

Other Federal Laws

Although OPA is the primary domestic legislation for oil spills, other federal laws contain provisions that relate to oil spills. Many of these provisions were in place before OPA. The following list is not all-inclusive, but it highlights the main requirements authorized by laws other than OPA.

Clean Water Act

The Clean Water Act (CWA) was the primary federal statute governing oil spills prior to OPA and many provisions continue to apply. A key provision is found in Section 311(b)(3), which prohibits the discharge of oil or hazardous substances into U.S. navigable waters. In addition, the CWA contains various penalty provisions for noncompliance, including violations of the discharge prohibition of Section 311(b).[84]

Pursuant to statutory requirements in the CWA,[85] the EPA crafted regulations[86] for spill prevention control and countermeasure (SPCC) plans in 1973. SPCC plans address the "procedures, methods, and equipment and other requirements for equipment to prevent discharges."[87] The EPA's SPCC plans apply only to non-transportation, onshore facilities that exceed a certain oil storage capacity and that, in the event of a spill, can be reasonably expected, because of their location, to produce an oil discharge that would reach navigable waters or adjoining shorelines of the United States.[88] Unlike other oil spill preparedness provisions, SPCC plans focus more on prevention than on response activities, requiring, for example, secondary containment (e.g., dikes, berms) for oil-storage equipment.

The agency offered several regulatory amendments after the 1973 rulemaking. Following the passage of the Oil Pollution Act of 1990 (OPA),[89] the agency proposed substantial changes and clarifications that were not made final until July 2002. For reasons beyond the scope of this report, the effective date of the 2002 final rule has been extended multiple times; for some parts of the amended rule, the current effective date was January 14, 2009, and for other parts, the effective date was extended to November 10, 2010.[90] However,

EPA proposed in July 2010 to extend the date an additional year for most facilities.[91]

Outer Continental Shelf Lands Act

The primary federal law governing oil development and operations in waters in federal jurisdiction is the Outer Continental Shelf Lands Act (OCSLA) of 1953 and its subsequent amendments (43 U.S.C. §§1331-1356). The OCSLA provided the foundation for regulations (30 C.F.R. Parts 250 and 550) that are implemented by the Bureau of Ocean Energy Management (BOEM) and the Bureau of Safety and Environmental Enforcement (BSEE).[92] Sections of these regulations address oil spill prevention and response issues by requiring that various equipment and procedures be in place at offshore facilities.[93]

Pipeline Statutes

The U.S. pipeline network is extensive. One estimate indicates there are more than 33,000 miles of pipelines just in the Gulf of Mexico.[94] Moreover, U.S. inland pipelines are concentrated in coastal areas, particularly in the Gulf states, and these pipelines may have an impact on coastal waters if spills reach waterways that empty into coastal waters.

Several laws govern oil pipelines. The Hazardous Liquid Pipeline Act of 1979 (P.L. 96-129) granted authority to the Department of Transportation (DOT) to regulate various issues regarding oil spills from pipelines. On December 29, 2006, the President signed the Pipeline Safety Improvement Act of 2006 (P.L. 109-468) to improve pipeline safety and security practices, and to reauthorize the federal Office of Pipeline Safety.[95] The Office of Pipeline Safety (OPS), which is part of the DOT, implements provisions concerning pipeline design, construction, operation and maintenance, and spill response planning.[96]

Vessel Statutes

Several federal laws directly or indirectly deal with oil pollution from vessels.[97] Laws concerning navigation reduce the possibilities of vessel collision or hull breach by objects in the waterways.[98] Other laws call for particular vessel design standards. For example, the Ports and Waterways Safety Act of 1972,[99] amended by the Port and Tanker Safety Act of 1978,[100] called for specific construction and equipment design requirements for oil tankers. (As noted, OPA subsequently amended this statute in 1990 to establish a phased-in schedule for double-hulled tankers.) Congress enacted the 1970s legislation to coincide with international initiatives. In fact, many of the federal laws concerning vessel standards and pollution control procedures were written to implement international conventions. These are discussed below.

RECENT PIPELINE SPILLS

Kalamazoo River—2010

On July 26, 2010, a pipeline released approximately 800,000 gallons of crude oil of oil into Michigan's Talmadge Creek, a waterway that flows into the Kalamazoo River. As the federal OSC (for the inland zone), EPA established a Unified Command of federal, state and local agencies, and private parties to respond to the spill. Pursuant to the liability provisions in OPA, Enbridge Energy Partners, LLP is the responsible party for the spill.

For more up-to-date information, see EPA's Enbridge oil spill website, at http://www.epa.gov/enbridgespill/index.html.

Yellowstone River—2011

On July 1, 2011, am ExxonMobil pipeline ruptured and released oil into the Yellowstone River near Billings, Montana. EPA leads the federal response activities, coordinating with Montana agencies and other federal agencies. According to the pipeline owner (and cited on EPA's website), the incident discharged an estimated 42,000 gallons.

For more up-to-date information, see EPA's Yellowstone River spill website at http://www.epa.gov/ yellowstoneriverspill/.

Federal Agencies' Responsibilities

The United States shares jurisdiction over its coastal waters with the coastal states. The 1953 Submerged Lands Act (SLA) gave coastal states jurisdiction over the submerged lands, waters, and natural resources (e.g., oil deposits) located, in most cases, within 3 nautical miles off the coastline.[101] The waters, seabed, and natural resources beyond the states' waters are exclusively federal, and extend to the edge of the exclusive economic zone (200 nautical miles from shore). However, the federal government maintains the authority to regulate commerce, navigation, national defense, power production, and international affairs within state waters.

The oil spill legal framework involves implementation by multiple federal agencies. Agency responsibilities can be divided into two categories: (1) oil spill response and cleanup and (2) oil spill prevention/preparedness.

Response

As mentioned above, the National Oil and Hazardous Substances Pollution Contingency Plan (NCP) contains the federal government's framework and operative requirements for responding to an oil spill (and releases of hazardous substances). Although first developed through administrative processes in 1968, subsequent laws have amended the NCP, including the Clean Water Act in 1972; the Comprehensive Environmental Response, Compensation, and Liability Act (CERCLA or Superfund) in 1980; and the Oil Pollution Act (OPA) in 1990. Oil spill response actions required under the regulations of the NCP are binding and enforceable, per these enforcement authorities.

The NCP establishes the National Response System (NRS), a multi-tiered and coordinated national response strategy for addressing oil spills and releases of hazardous substances. The NCP provisions specific to oil spill response are codified in 40 C.F.R. Part 300, Subpart D. Key components of the NRS include the following:

- National Response Team (NRT): composed of representatives from the federal departments and agencies assigned roles in responding to oil spills. The U.S. Coast Guard chairs the NRT when a response is being mounted to a spill in a coastal region.
- Regional Response Teams (RRTs): composed of regional representatives of each NRT member agency, state governments, and local governments. The Coast Guard leads the relevant RRT during responses to oil spills in coastal waters.
- Area Committees (ACs): composed of qualified personnel from federal, state, and local agencies. The primary function of each AC is to prepare an Area Contingency Plan (ACP) for its designated area.
- On-Scene Coordinator (OSC): who directs the response efforts and coordinates all other efforts at the scene.

Oil spill response authority is determined by the location of the spill: the Coast Guard has response authority in the coastal zone, and the EPA covers the inland zone.[102] The OSC has the ultimate authority to ensure that an oil spill is effectively removed and actions are taken to prevent further discharge from the source. The OSC is broadly empowered to direct and coordinate all response and recovery activities of federal, state, local, and private entities (including the responsible party), and will draw on resources available through the appropriate ACPs and RRTs.

Although the OSC must consult with designated trustees of natural resources and the governor of the state affected by the spill, the OSC has the authority and responsibility to determine when removal (i.e., cleanup) is complete.

Other agencies, particularly those on the NRT and relevant RRT, may play a role in response activities. As the chair of the NRT (and vice-chair during oil spills in the coastal zone), EPA may provide response support. For example, during the *Deepwater Horizon* spill response, EPA conducted air and water sampling and provided environmental monitoring support, particularly regarding the use of dispersants.

In addition, NOAA provides scientific analysis and consultation during oil spill response activities.[103] Assistance can include oil spill tracking, cleanup alternatives, and knowledge of at- risk natural resources. Moreover, NOAA experts begin to collect data to assess natural resource damages during response operations.

Prevention and Preparedness

Regarding oil spill prevention and preparedness duties, jurisdiction is determined by the potential sources (e.g., vessels, facilities, pipelines) of oil spills. A series of executive orders (EOs), coupled with memoranda of understanding (MOU), have established the various agency responsibilities.[104] **Table 1** identifies the agencies responsible for implementing prevention and preparedness regulations for the potential sources of oil spills.

Prevention responsibilities include, among other things, assessing whether facilities or vessels have the necessary equipment in place. As discussed above, vessels may be required to have double hulls; facilities may need secondary containment.

Preparedness duties involve oversight tasks, such as evaluating facility and vessel response plans. Preparedness responsibilities also include developing and maintaining contingency plans at various levels: area, regional, and national. Personnel training is a vital component of sustaining readiness. NOAA oil spill experts help train responders in government service and private business.

Table 1. Federal Agency Jurisdiction for Oil Spill Prevention and Preparedness Duties, by Source

Potential Source of Oil Spill	Responsible Agency
Vessels	Coast Guard
Onshore, non-transportation facilities	Environmental Protection Agency
Onshore, transportation facilities	Coast Guard and Department of Transportation
Deepwater ports[a]	Coast Guard and Department of Transportation
Offshore facilities (oil/gas extraction)	Bureau of Ocean Energy Management within the Department of Interior
Offshore pipelines directly associated with oil extraction activities (i.e., "production lines")[b]	Bureau of Ocean Energy Management within the Department of Interior
Offshore pipelines not directly associated with oil extraction activities (i.e., "transmission lines")	Office of Pipeline Safety within the Department of Transportation
Inland pipelines	Office of Pipeline Safety within the Department of Transportation

a. There is only one deepwater port for oil in U.S. coastal waters: the Louisiana Offshore Oil Port (LOOP).

b. For further discussion on federal pipeline jurisdiction, see National Research Council, *Improving the Safety of Marine Pipelines*, National Academies of Science, 1994, pp. 86-89.

In addition, OPA requires agencies to conduct internal examinations to test preparedness.[105] As part of this requirement, the Coast Guard conducts Spills of National Significance (SONS) exercises to analyze the Coast Guard's ability to respond to a major oil spill.

International Conventions

The relationship between international and domestic law can be complex. For example, a "self- executing" agreement taking the form of a treaty, signed by the Executive and ratified with the advice and consent of the Senate, stands on equal footing with federal statute. On the other hand, if an international agreement is not self-executing, implementing legislation may be necessary for the agreement's provisions to be given domestic legal effect, including to provide U.S. agencies with the domestic legal authority necessary to carry out functions contemplated under the agreement. Several federal laws governing oil spills were fashioned to implement obligations contained in international agreements.[106]

International conventions have played an important role in developing consistent standards for oil-carrying vessels from different nations. A primary player in this regard is the International Maritime Organization (IMO), a body of the United Nations, which sets international maritime vessel safety and marine pollution standards. The Coast Guard represents the United States at IMO meetings.

Multiple international conventions concern vessels and their impact on the marine environment. Described below are two selected conventions that contain provisions that are particularly relevant to oil pollution in coastal waters.

MARPOL 73/78

The IMO implements the 1973 International Convention for the Prevention of Pollution from Ships, as modified by the Protocol of 1978 (MARPOL 73/78).[107] Vessels whose nations are signatories to MARPOL are subject to its requirements, regardless of where they sail, and member nations are responsible for the vessels registered under their flag.

MARPOL 73/78 includes six annexes, each covering a different pollution type. Annex I (Prevention of Pollution by Oil) entered into force in 1983[108] and established requirements for controlling oil discharges to sea. Annex I requires vessels to have equipment that minimizes oil discharge, such as oil-water separators, and shipboard oil pollution emergency plans (SOPEPs). Although the SOPEP applicability is similar to that of the vessel response plan (VRP) required by OPA,[109] the purpose of the SOPEP is somewhat different. A SOPEP is intended to provide guidance to the vessel's officers regarding proper onboard emergency procedures when an oil spill occurs,[110] whereas the VRP is more focused on responding to the spill itself.

The United States implements Annex I through the Act to Prevent Pollution from Ships (APPS).[111] APPS applies to all U.S.-flagged ships, irrespective of location, and to all foreign- flagged vessels in U.S. waters or at ports under U.S. jurisdiction. The Coast Guard issues and enforces regulations necessary to carry out the APPS provisions. The Coast Guard inspection program is a key component of its oil spill prevention effort.

Intervention Convention

The 1967 *Torrey Canyon* spill off the coast of Great Britain was one of the first major spills to receive worldwide attention.[112] The incident raised many questions regarding oil spill response, particularly when dealing with vessels from other nations. For example, the incident prompted debate over responses allowable if a nation's waters and environment are threatened by a spill from another nation's vessel. The 1969 International Convention Relating to Intervention on the High Seas in Cases of Oil Pollution Casualties (the Intervention Convention) sought to address these issues.

To implement this convention in the United States, Congress passed the Intervention on the High Seas Act of 1974.[113] Under this act, if the Coast Guard determines there to be a "grave and imminent danger to the coastline or related interests of the United States from pollution or threat of pollution of the sea by convention oil [i.e., as defined in the convention]," the Coast Guard can take action to "prevent, mitigate, or eliminate that danger."

State Laws

As mentioned above, multiple states had oil spill liability laws before the passage of OPA in 1990. During the 15 years prior to OPA's passage, the issue of whether or not to preempt state liability laws was perhaps the primary obstacle to enacting unified oil spill legislation. Proponents of preemption argued that differing state laws—particularly the various levels of liability—frustrate the shipping industry and were contrary to the goal of comprehensive federal legislation.

Preemption opponents maintained that states should be allowed (as with most other federal environmental statutes) to set stiffer standards regarding liability, compensation, and cleanup.[114] In the aftermath of the *Exxon Valdez* spill, the scales tipped to the side of anti-preemption. According to OPA Section 1018 (referred to as a "savings clause"), the act will not preempt any state from imposing "additional liability or requirements" with respect to the discharge of oil or related response activity (e.g., cleanup standards). A 2003 study identified 16 states that impose unlimited liability for oil spills.[115]

There was some concern that the language of OPA's savings clause would allow states to regulate matters typically reserved for the federal government, such as oil tanker construction. To address this issue, the conference report stated that the savings clause would not disturb a 1978 Supreme Court decision that dealt with the intersection of federal and state authority to regulate the shipping industry.[116] In that case, the Court determined that a Washington State law was preempted. The state law had attempted to govern oil tanker design, size, and movement in Puget Sound.[117]

Regardless of the clarification in the conference report, the line between federal and state jurisdiction (i.e., the extent of federal preemption) continues to be tested. In 2000, the Supreme Court struck down (as preempted) a Washington State rule calling for various personnel requirements, such as training, on oil tankers.[118] Similarly, in March 2010, a federal district court in Massachusetts ruled against a state law—finding it preempted—that would affect tanker design, personnel qualifications, and navigation.[119]

CONCLUSION

With the nation a significant producer and consumer of oil, vast quantities are continuously extracted, imported, and transported throughout the United States. Oil is expected to remain a primary source of energy in the United States for at least the next several decades. Future oil spills are inevitable.

As with the *Exxon Valdez* oil spill in 1989, the 2010 *Deepwater Horizon* spill generated significant attention to various oil spill policy matters, including prevention, preparedness, response, and liability and compensation. Members held multiple hearings and introduced numerous bills in the 111th Congress. The 111th Congress enacted three oil spill-related proposals into law (P.L. 111-191, P.L. 111-212, and P.L. 111-281), but these laws generally concerned short-term matters that will not have a lasting impact on oil spill governance.[120]

In general, oil spill-related issues garnered less attention during the 112th Congress. The 112th Congress enacted two statutes that contain oil spill-related provisions.[121]

- On January 3, 2012, the President signed P.L. 112-90 (the Pipeline Safety, Regulatory Certainty, and Job Creation Act of 2011), which included several oil spill-related provisions involving pipelines.
- On July 6, 2012, the President signed P.L. 112-141 (MAP-21), which includes a subtitle referred to as the RESTORE Act. The RESTORE Act establishes the Gulf Coast Restoration Fund in the General Treasury. Eighty percent of any administrative and civil Clean Water

Act Section 311 penalties paid by responsible parties in connection with the 2010 *Deepwater Horizon* oil spill will provide the revenues for the fund. Through several different mechanisms, the fund will support environmental and economic restoration in the Gulf states.

APPENDIX. FEDERAL AUTHORITIES BEFORE AND AFTER THE *EXXON VALDEZ* SPILL

The following list highlights the primary federal authorities that were in effect when the *Exxon Valdez* spill occurred in 1989:

- Clean Water Act (1972): The Clean Water Act (CWA) represented the broadest authority for addressing oil spills at the time of the *Exxon Valdez* spill. Section 311 of the CWA established requirements for oil spill reporting, response, and liability. The act also created a fund (311 Fund), maintained by federal appropriations, that could be used for cleanup and natural resource restoration.
- Deepwater Port Act (1974):[122] This statute addressed oil spills and liability issues at deepwater oil ports. The act also set up the Deepwater Port Fund to provide for prompt cleanup and to compensate damages above liability limits. The fund was financed by a per-gallon tax on oil transferred at a deepwater port.
- Trans-Alaska Pipeline Authorization Act (1973):[123] This act covered oil spills and liability relating to the Trans-Alaska Pipeline System (TAPS). Although the pipeline is constructed over land, spills from it could reach coastal waters via inland rivers. The act created a trust fund, financed through a lessee fee, that could be used to respond to spills and damages from the pipeline.
- Outer Continental Shelf Lands Act Amendments (1978):[124] This act established an oil spill liability structure and rules for oil extraction facilities in federal offshore waters. With this legislation, Congress created the Offshore Pollution Fund, financed by a per-gallon fee on produced oil, that could be used for oil spill cleanup and damages.
- National Oil and Hazardous Substances Pollution Contingency Plan (NCP): The first NCP was administratively prepared in 1968 after observing the British government's response to a 37-million-gallon oil tanker spill (*Torrey Canyon*) off the coast of England.[125] The NCP

contains the federal government's procedures for responding to oil spills and hazardous substance releases.[126]

After the *Exxon Valdez* spill, many observers[127] described the above legal collection as an ineffective patchwork. Arguably, each law had perceived shortcomings (discussed below in the context of post-*Exxon Valdez* legislation), and none provided comprehensive oil spill coverage.

For more than 15 years prior to the *Exxon Valdez* incident, Congress made attempts to enact a unified oil pollution law. Several contentious issues produced deadlocks, hindering the passage of legislation. One of the central points of debate, state preemption, dealt with whether a federal oil spill law should limit a state's ability to impose stricter requirements, particularly unlimited liability. Other liability questions also generated debate. For example, if an oil spill occurred, should the owner of the cargo (i.e., oil) be held liable, as was the ship owner/operator? Another point of contention was whether oil-carrying vessels should be required to have double hulls. Although proponents argued that a second hull would help prevent oil spills, the shipping industry raised concern that implementing such a mandate would disrupt oil transportation and potentially affect the national economy. A final issue involved the interaction between domestic legislation (federal and state) and international measures. Some were concerned that if the United States became a party to certain international agreements under consideration in the 1980s,[128] the international standards would preempt federal and state laws, especially those establishing liability limits. Proponents argued that these concerns were overstated and stressed that joining the international agreements was especially important for the United States because of the international nature of oil transportation and associated pollution.

End Notes

[1] Energy Information Administration, *Annual Energy Review*, Primary Energy Consumption Estimates by Source, 1949–2011, September 2012, at http://www.eia.gov/totalenergy/data/annual/#summary.

[2] Note that the *Exxon Valdez* spill ranks only 35th for spill volume on the list of international tanker spills since 1967. See International Tanker Owners Pollution Federation Limited, Historical Data, at http://www.itopf.com/stats.html.

[3] See National Research Council (NRC), *Oil in the Sea III: Inputs, Fates, and Effects*, National Academies of Science (hereinafter "NRC report"), February 2003, p. 11.

[4] In this report, "oil" refers to crude oil and petroleum products, including gasoline and other fuels, unless stated otherwise.

[5] For the purposes of this report, "U.S. coastal waters" is defined broadly to encompass all waters between the shore and the boundary of the U.S. exclusive economic zone (200 nautical miles from shore). Note that in other documents, "coastal" may refer only to state waters, but in this report, the term "coastal waters" includes state and federally regulated waters.

[6] Although oil spills certainly occur in or reach non-coastal U.S. waters, this report focuses on issues and background information related to coastal water spills. However, in many cases, the issues overlap.

[7] NRC report, pp. 67-88.

[8] The NRC estimate for natural seep volume ranges from 24 million to 71 million gallons each year. The "best estimate" (included in **Figure 1**) is 47 million gallons (p. 69).

[9] NRC report, p. 2.

[10] This subcategory is particularly broad: municipal wastewaters, non-refinery industrial discharge, refinery discharges, urban runoff, river discharges, and ocean dumping.

[11] Includes large vessels, such as oil tankers, and smaller vessels, such as fishing boats.

[12] Includes motor boats, jet skis, and other recreational vessels.

[13] Atmospheric deposition generally refers to the process of air pollutants (generated from petroleum combustion) reaching water bodies through various mechanisms (e.g., precipitation). According to the NRC report, "atmospheric deposition supplies hydrocarbons somewhat uniformly to the coastal ocean at relatively low loading rates over large areas" (p. 115).

[14] Based on average, annual releases from 1990-1999. NRC report, pp. 69, 87.

[15] Other sources include non-tanker vessels (e.g., cargo ships, passenger vessels, fishing vessels, and recreational vessels) and unknown sources. For a complete list see the USCG Oil Spill Compendium at https://homeport.uscg.mil (click on "Investigations").

[16] As of the date of this report, the Coast Guard Oil Spill Compendium includes comprehensive data through 2009. This database has been updated periodically, but not on an annual basis.

[17] P.L. 96-478, 33 U.S.C. §1901 et seq. These standards and the U.S. law are discussed later in this report.

[18] The *Exxon Valdez* spill tallied approximately $2 billion in cleanup costs and $1 billion in natural resource damages (not including third-party claims)—in 1990 dollars. Punitive damage claims were litigated for more than 12 years, eventually reaching the U.S. Supreme Court in 2008 (*Exxon Shipping v. Baker*, 128 S. Ct. 2605 (2008)). Plaintiffs were eventually awarded approximately $500 million in punitive damages. An additional $500 million in interest on those damages was subsequently awarded.

[19] CRS Report (out-of-print, available from CRS by request), *Liability Provisions in State Oil Spill Laws: A Brief Summary*, October 1, 1990.

[20] For example, California passed the Lempert-Keene-Seastrand Oil Spill Prevention and Response Act in 1990. More information is available at http://www.dfg.ca.gov/ospr/about/history.html#.

[21] While oil extraction activities contribute approximately 1% of the total oil input to North American waters, the vast majority (95%) of this (1%) oil extraction input comes from operational discharges, which are regulated by a Clean Water Act permit system. NRC Report, Table 3-2.

[22] NRC report, p. 33.

[23] National Incident Command's Flow Rate Technical Group estimate of August 2, 2010.

[24] For a list of the largest oil tanker spills, see The International Tanker Owners Pollution Federation (ITOPF) website, at http://www.itopf.com/.

[25] NRC report, p. 4.

[26] These "sub-lethal" effects can occur at concentrations that are several orders of magnitude lower than concentrations that cause death. NRC report, p. 127.

[27] NRC report, Chapter 5; also multiple conversations with National Oceanic and Atmospheric Administration (NOAA) personnel (2008).

[28] NRC report, p. 120.

[29] NRC report, p. 121.

[30] NRC report, p. 134.

[31] See, for example, Terry Hazen et al., "Deep-Sea Plume Enriches Indigenous Oil-Degrading Bacteria," *Science* (Online), August 24, 2010; Richard Camilli et al., "Tracking Hydrocarbon Plume Transport and Biodegradation at *Deepwater Horizon*," *Science* (Online), August 19, 2010.

[32] For example, the November 7, 2007, spill (53,000 gallons) from a container ship into the San Francisco Bay generated considerable interest.

[33] The average cleanup cost is three times higher in the United States than in Europe (based on 1997 data and *excluding* the Exxon Valdez costs). See Etkin, Dagmar, "Estimating Cleanup Costs for Oil Spills," paper presented at the 1999 International Oil Spill Conference, 1999, citing data from the Oil Spill Intelligence Report International Oil Spill Database.

[34] This is primarily due to the fact that a spill of any size (e.g., in a sensitive area) will require that equipment and response experts be sent to the scene. See Etkin, Dagmar, "Estimating Cleanup Costs for Oil Spills," paper presented at the 1999 International Oil Spill Conference, 1999, p. 5.

[35] For more information, see NOAA's Damage Assessment, Remediation, and Restoration Program at http://www.darrp.noaa.gov/about/index.html.

[36] 33 U.S.C. §2706(c). In some cases, trustees may share responsibility over the same resource. See, for example, Department of the Interior's "Pollution Response and Natural Resource Trusteeship Training Module On NRDA," at http://www.doi.gov/oepc/response/a01.htm.

[37] 33 U.S.C. §2712 and Executive Order (EO) 12777 (October 18, 1991).

[38] 33 U.S.C. §2706(d).

[39] 61 *Federal Register* 440 (January 5, 1996). See also NOAA, *Injury Assessment Guidance Document for Natural Resource Damage Assessment Under the Oil Pollution Act of 1990* (1996).

[40] See 15 C.F.R. §990.30, definition of "value."

[41] 33 U.S.C. §2706(f); William D. Brighton, *Natural Resource Damages under the Comprehensive Environmental Response, Compensation, and Liability Act* (2006), U.S. Department of Justice, Environment and Natural Resources Division.

[42] William D. Brighton, *Natural Resource Damages under the Comprehensive Environmental Response, Compensation, and Liability Act* (2006), U.S. Department of Justice, Environment and Natural Resources Division.

[43] A handful of other oil spills followed the *Exxon Valdez* in 1989 and 1990 (e.g., the *Mega Borg* spilled 5 million gallons of oil in the Gulf of Mexico), further spurring congressional action.

[44] P.L. 101-380, primarily codified at U.S.C. §2701 et seq.

[45] The official statutory name is the Federal Water Pollution Control Act, P.L. 92-500, as amended, codified at 33 U.S.C. §1251 et seq.

[46] See, for example, Wilkinson, Cynthia et al., "Slick Work: An Analysis of the Oil Pollution Act of 1990," *Journal of Energy, Natural Resources, and Environmental Law*, 12 (1992), p. 190.

[47] See Grumbles, Benjamin, and Manley, Joan, "The Oil Pollution Act of 1990: Legislation in the Wake of a Crisis," *Natural Resources and Environment*, 10:2 (1995), p. 38.

[48] Leading up to the passage of OPA, parties referred to this approach as "federalizing" the spill.

[49] U.S. Congress, House Committee on Merchant Marine and Fisheries, Report accompanying H.R. 1465, Oil Pollution Prevention, Removal, Liability, and Compensation Act of 1989, 1989, H.Rept. 101-242, Part 2, 101st Cong., 1st sess., p. 84.

[50] OPA §1011.

[51] See EPA "National Contingency Plan Overview" at http://www.epa.gov/emergencies/content/lawsregs/ncpover.htm.

[52] The NCP is codified at 40 C.F.R. Part 300.

[53] OPA §4202, amending §311(j) of the CWA.

[54] OPA §4201(b), amending §311(d)(2)(J) of the CWA.

[55] The response plan requirement is applicable only to an onshore facility that, because of its location, could reasonably be expected to cause substantial harm to the environment by discharging into navigable waters, adjoining shorelines, or the exclusive economic zone. CWA §311(j)(5)(iii).

[56] OPA §4202, amending §311(j)(5)(E) of the CWA.

[57] U.S. Congress, House Committee on Merchant Marine and Fisheries, Report accompanying H.R. 1465, Oil Pollution Prevention, Removal, Liability, and Compensation Act of 1989, 1989, H.Rept. 101-242, Part 2, 101st Cong., 1st sess., p. 87. OPA §4202, amending §311(j)(5)(C)(iii) of the CWA.

[58] Amendments Relating to the Oil Pollution Act of 1990, Title VII of Coast Guard and Maritime Transportation Act of 2004 (P.L. 108-293), codified at 33 U.S.C. §1321.

[59] Primarily the shipboard oil pollution emergency plans required by MARPOL 73/78, discussed later in this report.

[60] A study from the National Academy of Sciences reached this conclusion in 1999. See National Research Council, *Double hull Tanker Legislation: An Assessment of the Oil Pollution Act of 1990*, National Academies of Science, 1999, p. 144.

[61] Opponents maintained that if water entered the space between hulls, the ship could become unstable, hindering salvage and possibly capsizing. Cynthia Wilkinson et al., "Slick Work: An Analysis of the Oil Pollution Act of 1990," *Journal of Energy, Natural Resources, and Environmental Law*, 12 (1992), p. 196.

[62] U.S. Congress, Conference Report accompanying H.R. 1465, Oil Pollution Act of 1990, H. Conf. Rept. 101-653, at 140-141 (1990).

[63] OPA §4115, amending 46 U.S.C. §3703.

[64] This exception applied to many inland barges.

[65] Lightering is the process of transferring oil from a large vessel to a smaller vessel. This common practice occurs in designated areas that are typically many miles away from shore.

[66] For a discussion of liability issues raised by the 2010 *Deepwater Horizon* oil spill, see CRS Report R41679, *Liability and Compensation Issues Raised by the 2010 Gulf Oil Spill*, by Jonathan L. Ramseur.

[67] The definition of "facility" is broadly worded and includes pipelines and motor vehicles. OPA §1001.

[68] Under the pre-OPA regime (primarily the CWA), a discharge 12 miles beyond shore had to affect the natural resources before liability attached. Under OPA §1002, the discharge itself triggers liability. Cynthia Wilkinson et al., "Slick Work: An Analysis of the Oil Pollution Act of 1990," *Journal of Energy, Natural Resources, and Environmental Law*, 12 (1992), p. 201.

[69] U.S. Congress, House Committee on Merchant Marine and Fisheries, Report accompanying H.R. 1465, Oil Pollution Prevention, Removal, Liability, and Compensation Act of 1989, 1989, H.Rept. 101-242, Part 2, 101st Cong., 1st sess., p. 31.

[70] OPA §1002(b)(1).

[71] OPA §1002(b)(2).

[72] Section 107(b) of the Comprehensive Environmental Response, Compensation, and Liability Act (CERCLA, commonly known as Superfund), P.L. 96-510.

[73] In addition, liability limits are unavailable if the violation of a federal safety, construction, or operating requirement proximately caused the spill. Spillers must also report the incident and cooperate with response officials to take advantage of the liability caps. OPA §1004(c).

[74] 37,895 gross tons x $1,200/ton = $45.47 million. Vessel data from United States Coast Guard, *Investigation into the Striking of Submerged Objects by the Tank Vessel Athos I in the Delaware River on November 26, 2004 with a Major Discharge of Oil*, January 2006, p. 4.

[75] U.S. Coast Guard, "Consumer Price Index Adjustments of Oil Pollution Act of 1990 Limits of Liability—Vessels and Deepwater Ports," *Federal Register* Volume 74, No. 125 (July 1, 2009), pp. 31357-31369.

[76] 33 U.S.C. 2704(b).

[77] Wilkinson, Cynthia et al., "Slick Work: An Analysis of the Oil Pollution Act of 1990," *Journal of Energy, Natural Resources, and Environmental Law*, 12 (1992), p. 188.

[78] U.S. Congress, House Committee on Merchant Marine and Fisheries, Report accompanying H.R. 1465, Oil Pollution Prevention, Removal, Liability, and Compensation Act of 1989, 1989, H.Rept. 101-242, Part 2, 101st Cong., 1st sess., p. 35.

[79] Omnibus Budget Reconciliation Act of 1986 (P.L. 99-509).

[80] The CWA §311(k) revolving fund; the Deepwater Port Liability Fund; the Trans-Alaska Pipeline Liability Fund; and the Offshore Oil Pollution Compensation Fund.

[81] Omnibus Budget Reconciliation Act of 1989 (P.L. 101-239). Other revenue sources for the fund include interest on the fund, cost recovery from the parties responsible for the spills, and any fines or civil penalties collected.

[82] Section 405 of P.L. 110-343.

[83] This amount is significantly less than the 4.9 million barrels estimated to have been released during the 2010 Gulf spill. See National Incident Command's Flow Rate Technical Group, press release, August 2, 2010.

[84] For further discussion, see CRS Report R41370, *Federal Civil and Criminal Penalties Possibly Applicable to Parties Responsible for the Gulf of Mexico Oil Spill*, by Robert Meltz.

[85] Section 311(j)(1) of the 1972 CWA called for regulations to prevent the discharge of oil from vessels, onshore facilities, and offshore facilities. Executive Order 11735 (August 3, 1973) granted EPA the authority to regulate non- transportation-related onshore and offshore facilities.

[86] U.S. EPA, "Oil Pollution Prevention: Non-Transportation Related Onshore and Offshore Facilities," *Federal Register*, vol. 38, no. 237 (December 11, 1973), pp. 34164-34170.

[87] CWA §311(j)(1)(C).

[88] See 40 C.F.R. §112.1.

[89] P.L. 101-380, primarily codified at U.S.C. §2701 et seq.

[90] For a comprehensive history of the regulations, see *Federal Register*, vol. 74, pp. 58784 (November 13, 2009).

[91] For more information, see EPA's SPCC website at http://www.epa.gov/emergencies/content/spcc/index.htm.

[92] These agencies replaced the former Minerals Management Service (MMS). On May 19, 2010, the Secretary of the Department of the Interior (DOI) replaced the MMS with the Bureau of Ocean Energy Management, Regulation, and Enforcement (BOEMRE). On October 1, 2011, DOI divided BOEMRE into three separate entities: the Bureau of Ocean Energy Management (BOEM), the Bureau of Safety and Environmental Enforcement (BSEE), and the Office of Natural Resources Revenue (ONRR).

[93] For more information, see CRS Report RL33404, *Offshore Oil and Gas Development: Legal Framework*, by Adam Vann.

[94] See, for example, MMS Press Release from February 2, 2005, at http://www.mms.gov/ooc/press/2005/ press0202.htm.

[95] See 49 U.S.C. §60101 et seq.

[96] For further information on pipeline legislation, see CRS Report R41536, *Keeping America's Pipelines Safe and Secure: Key Issues for Congress*, by Paul W. Parfomak.

[97] For a comprehensive list of federal maritime legislation see USCG, *Marine Safety Manual*, Vol. IX (undated), Chapter 1, available at http://homeport.uscg.mil.

[98] For example, the Rivers and Harbors Act of 1899, as amended (33 U.S.C. §401 et seq.), and the International Regulations for Preventing Collisions at Sea, as amended (33 U.S.C. §1601 et seq.).

[99] P.L. 92-340, 33 U.S.C. §1221 et seq.

[100] P.L. 95-474, codified at 33 U.S.C. §§1221-1232 and 46 U.S.C. §§3701-3718.

[101] Most state waters extend 3 nautical miles (1 nautical mile = 6,076 feet, or 1.15 miles) from shore. Louisiana waters extend 3 imperial nautical miles (1 imperial nautical mile = 6,080 feet). Texas and Gulf Coast of Florida waters extend 3 marine leagues (equating to 9

nautical miles). See the MMS, OCS, website ("Definitions and Jurisdictions") at http://www.mms.gov/incidents/pollution.htm. See also CRS Report RL33404, *Offshore Oil and Gas Development: Legal Framework*, by Adam Vann.

[102] The terms inland zone and coastal zone are defined in the National Contingency Plan (40 C.F.R. §300.5). The coastal zone covers all waters subject to the tide, the Great Lakes, and all seaward waters (extending 200 nautical miles beyond shore). The inland zone covers all other U.S. waters. Spills in inland waters can potentially affect coastal waters and ecosystems, particularly if the spill occurs in water systems near the coast. In fact, a fine line may separate specific inland and coastal waters (e.g., consider the nexus between a bay and a river).

[103] For more information see NOAA's Office of Response and Restoration website, at http://response.restoration.noaa.gov/index.php.

[104] Executive Order (EO) 12777 (October 18, 1991) delegates authorities pursuant to the Oil Pollution Act of 1990. This order was amended by EO 13286 (March 5, 2003), which reorganized duties in response to the creation of the Department of Homeland Security.

[105] As required by OPA §4202(a), which amended CWA §311(j)(7), codified in 33 U.S.C. §1321(j)(7).

[106] If a treaty is considered "self-executing," domestic legislation implementing the treaty is not necessary. For more details on these issues, see CRS Report RL32528, *International Law and Agreements: Their Effect Upon U.S. Law*, by Michael John Garcia.

[107] For convention texts and other materials, see http://www.imo.org.

[108] The phrase "entry into force" signifies that the requisite number of nations have ratified the convention or annex, thus making the agreed upon requirements binding for all participating nations. For more discussion of the procedures of international conventions, see the IMO website at http://www.imo.org.

[109] All vessels of any type over 400 gross tons traveling over international waters must have a SOPEP approved by their flag state. See USCG VRP/SOPEP "FAQs" at http://www. uscg.mil/vrp.

[110] USCG, 1997, *Marine Safety Manual, Marine Environment Protection, Volume IX*, p. 4-24.

[111] P.L. 96-478, 33 U.S.C. §1901 et seq.

[112] The *Torrey Canyon*, a Liberian-flagged tanker, spilled approximately 35 million gallons of crude oil.

[113] P.L. 93-248 , 33 U.S.C. §1471 et seq.

[114] One argument against preemption was that existing requirements under particular state laws would be diminished or negated entirely. See Benjamin Grumbles and Joan Manley, "The Oil Pollution Act of 1990: Legislation in the Wake of a Crisis," *Natural Resources and Environment*, 10:2 (1995), p. 38.

[115] Dagmar Etkin, 2003, *A Worldwide Review of Marine Oil Spill Fines and Penalties*, at http://www.environmental- research.com/erc_papers/ERC_paper_10.pdf. See also, CRS Congressional Distribution Memorandum, "Oil Spill Liability in the Gulf States," July 2, 2010 (on file with author).

[116] U.S. Congress, Conference Report accompanying H.R. 1465, Oil Pollution Act of 1990, H. Conf. Rept. 101-653, at 122 (1990).

[117] *Ray v. Atlantic Richfield*, 435 U.S. 151 (1978).

[118] *United States v. Locke*, 529 U.S. 89 (2000).

[119] *United States v. Massachusetts*, 2010 Westlaw 1345018 (D. Mass. March 31, 2010).

[120] See CRS Report R41453, *Oil Spill Legislation in the 111th Congress*, by Jonathan L. Ramseur.

[121] See CRS Report R41684, *Enacted and Proposed Oil Spill Legislation in the 112th Congress*, by Jonathan L. Ramseur.

[122] P.L. 93-627, codified at 33 U.S.C. §1501 et seq.

[123] P.L. 93-153, codified at 43 U.S.C. §1651 et seq.

[124] P.L. 95-372, codified at 43 U.S.C. §1801 et seq.

[125] See EPA "National Contingency Plan Overview" at http://www.epa.gov/emergencies/content/lawsregs/ncpover.htm.

[126] The NCP is codified at 40 C.F.R. Part 300.

[127] See, for example, U.S. Congress, House Committee on Merchant Marine and Fisheries, Report accompanying H.R. 1465, Oil Pollution Prevention, Removal, Liability, and Compensation Act of 1989, 1989, H.Rept. 101-242, Part 2, 101st Cong., 1st sess., p. 32.

[128] The two agreements under consideration were the 1984 Protocols to the International Convention on Civil Liability for Oil Pollution Damage and the Protocols to the International Fund for Compensation for Oil Pollution Damages.

INDEX